The Rocks and Mountains of Cape Town

The Rocks and Mountains of Cape Town

John S. Compton

DOUBLE
STOREY
a juta company

to Lisa & Ross

Second impression 2006
First published 2004
by Double Storey Books,
a division of Juta & Co. Ltd,
Mercury Crescent, Wetton,
Cape Town, South Africa

© 2004 John S. Compton

ISBN 1-919930-70-1

Editing by Helen Laurenson
Page design and layout by Jenny Sandler
Cover design by Toby Newsome
Printing by ABC Press, Epping, Cape Town

Contents

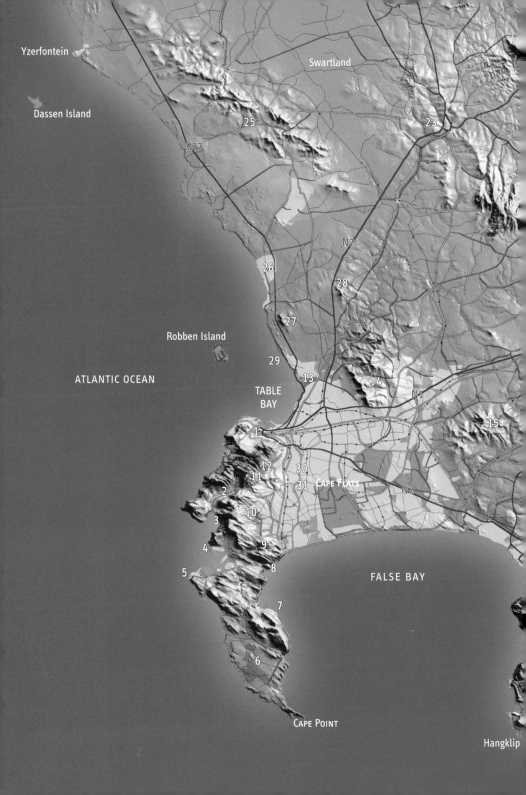

Yzerfontein

Dassen Island

Swartland

25

R27

23

N7

26

28

27

Robben Island

29

13

14

N1

ATLANTIC OCEAN

TABLE
BAY

15

1

12

11

30

31

Cape Flats

N2

2

10

3

9

4

8

5

7

FALSE BAY

6

Cape Point

Hangklip

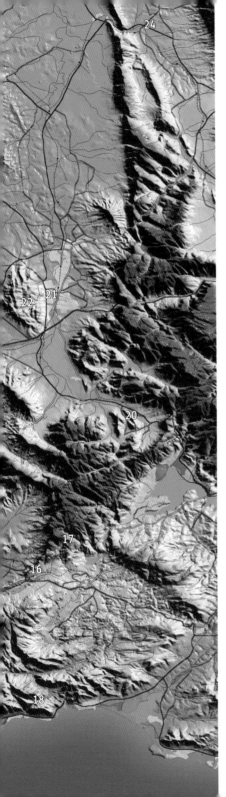

Figure 1. Topographic road map of
Cape Town and the surrounding areas.

1   CBD
2   Disa River/Hout Bay
3   Chapman's Peak Drive
4   Noordhoek Beach
5   Kommetjie
6   Cape of Good Hope Reserve
7   Simon's Town/Boulders Beach
8   Fish Hoek
9   Peers Cave
10 Cecilia Plantation
11 Kirstenbosch Botanical Gardens
12 Rhodes Memorial
13 Rietvlei
14 Tygerberg
15 Bottelaryberg
16 Sir Lowry's Pass
17 Hottentots Holland Mountains
18 Kogelberg Reserve
19 Stellenbosch
20 Franschhoek
21 Paarl
22 Paarl Rock
23 Malmesbury
24 Tulbagh
25 Darling Hills
26 Koeberg Nuclear Power Station
27 Blouberg
28 Koeberg
29 Bloubergstrand
30 Rondebosch Common
31 Kenilworth Racecourse

Preface

After learning that I am a geologist, acquaintances often approach me with a question about a rock exposure they have seen on a hike or Sunday drive, or present me with a rock that has struck their curiosity. I have come to realise that many people besides the students I teach at university are interested in the rocks and mountains that they see every day on their way to work or on weekend outdoor excursions. It is for these people that this book has been written.

My aim is to provide a basic guide to the rocks and mountains that are so spectacularly on display in the Cape Town area. No prior knowledge of the earth sciences is assumed, and any essential scientific concepts and processes are briefly explained in separate text boxes. The emphasis is on the greater Cape Town area, but easily accessed and popular areas of the Western Cape, most within an hour's drive of Cape Town, are also included (Fig. 1).

Figure 2. The city of Cape Town sits nestled within the City Bowl, a large mountainous amphitheatre that opens to the sea at the northern end of the Cape Peninsula. The suburbs of the city sprawl out over most of the Cape Flats to the east (left).

Part of the joy of visiting or living in Cape Town is the ever-present, dramatic mountain vistas and beautiful rock exposures one views while walking in the mountains or along the coast (Fig. 2). I hope that this book will add new insights and a dimension of understanding that increase both the pleasure of being in Cape Town and a sense of 'connectedness' to the environment. In so doing, my objective has not been to diminish the mystique, but rather to enhance the awe; to get people thinking about and engaged in their surroundings. The main focus of the book is on the deep, geologic time of the rocks and mountains, but I have also integrated the story of the relationship of the landscape, plants and people to the rocks. In this way this book ties into the number of excellent guides available on the natural history, flora, people and hiking trails of the area. It is this interdisciplinary approach that yields a more holistic and deeper understanding critical to our appreciation and responsible use of our natural world.

CHAPTER 1

Understanding the landscape

Figure 3. The Cape Town landscape viewed from the sea. The prominent vertical sandstone cliffs rise to the east as the sharp Devil's Peak and to the south as the flat-topped Table Mountain. The rounded knob of Lion's Head and softly rounded Lion's Rump (Signal Hill) above Sea Point and the V&A Waterfront lie to the west.

Mountains rising up from the Flats

Whether you are approaching Cape Town from a ship at sea, descending to land in an aircraft or driving in along one of the national motor routes, Table Mountain makes the first and most striking announcement of your arrival. What makes Table Mountain so impressive is the near-vertical relief of over 1 000 m as it rises from the sea to a top that from most approaches looks nearly flat, as if a large block of Earth had popped up from below (Fig. 3). In strong contrast, and emphasising the flat mountain top, are the nearby Devil's Peak to the east and the rounded knob of Lion's Head, separated from Table Mountain by the deep Kloofnek saddle.

Once you are in Cape Town, there are many good vantage points for viewing the surrounding landforms (Fig. 4). Most of these viewpoints are easily reached by car, such as the top of Signal Hill, Tafelberg Road beyond the cableway station, Rhodes Memorial above Rondebosch, or Bloubergstrand with its overviews of Table Mountain across Table Bay. But the best views are to be had from outside the car, and there are many hiking trails at all levels of altitude and difficulty within easy reach of Cape Town, from which to take in the scenery. You can reach the top of Table Mountain by following any number

Figure 4. Cape Town road map and topography, showing the location of good viewing sites.

1 Cableway	7 Green Point	13 Mowbray Ridge / King's Blockhouse
2 Tafelberg Road	8 Devil's Peak	14 Twelve Apostles
3 Lion's Head	9 Platteklip Gorge	15 Newlands Forest
4 CBD	10 Camps Bay	16 Bantry Bay / Sea Point Contact
5 V&A Waterfront	11 Kloofnek	17 Sea Point Promenade
6 Signal Hill	12 Maclear's Beacon	

Figure 5. Moonrise over Devil's Peak as seen from the top of Lion's Head. The lower slopes of Mowbray Ridge rise gently to the rugged cliff faces above. The lights of the City Bowl are in the foreground and of the Cape Flats in the background.

of trails in a vigorous and steep three- to four-hour hike or by taking a quick trip up the cableway. And the one- to two-hour hike to the top of Lion's Head is popular for watching the sunset, followed by a moonlit descent after a full moon has risen over the mountains to the east (Fig. 5).

From many of these viewing sites, you can see more distant but equally striking features. On a clear day the view to the east of Cape Town out across the Cape Flats reveals the Hottentots Holland as well as other mountain ranges (Fig. 6), whose highest peaks of 2 200 m are occasionally powdered with snow after a winter front. Lying east-northeast from Cape Town, in the foreground of the distant mountains, are the gently rolling hills of Tygerberg and Bottelaryberg, with the more distant but notable hills of Koeberg and Blouberg situated to the west (Fig. 1). Hills similar to the Tygerberg also form the foothills that butt up against many of the cliff-faced mountains: Signal Hill and Mowbray Ridge surrounding the City Bowl, for example, as well as many of the vineyards surrounding Stellenbosch. Looking south from the top of Table Mountain, you can see spectacular rock-cliff exposures stretching down the length of the Cape

Figure 6. Sunrise over the still-illuminated Cape Flats as seen from Rhodes Memorial, with the rounded hills of the Bottelaryberg silhouetted against the Hottentots Holland and other mountains along the distant skyline.

Peninsula. These mountain cliff-face exposures, impressive even at a distance, can be viewed up close along the roads that encircle the Cape Peninsula or on the wine routes of Stellenbosch and Franschhoek to the northeast.

In contrast to and accentuating the steep mountain terrains are the Cape Flats, the low-lying expanse of land that stretches between the mountains of the Cape Peninsula and the mountains to the east. And if you look north to the white arch of the beach of Table Bay, you can see Robben Island looking precariously flat as it rises only 30 m above the sea. The sea can also be seen further to the south at False Bay. It is easy to imagine the sea flooding the Cape Flats and cutting off the Cape Peninsula from the rest of Africa to form a large offshore island, as it did during periods of higher sea level in the past.

How did this diverse landscape of rocky, cliff-faced mountains, large, gently rolling hills and extensive flat lands come to be, and why do the landforms differ so strikingly one from the other? Did Table Mountain pop up from below or is it a resistant remnant that persisted after the surrounding rocks were worn away?

To answer these questions, it helps to step back and place the landscape of the Cape Town area within the large-scale framework of the geological features of southern Africa. If we take a big step back and observe southern Africa from space (Fig. 7), Table Mountain and the Hottentots Holland Mountains turn out to be part of a much larger mountain chain that extends 700 km from Port Elizabeth running parallel to the coast to Cape Town, where it takes a sharp 90 degree turn to continue 150 km north of Cape Town as the Cederberg. This long mountain chain is referred to as the Cape Fold Belt (Fig. 8) and is made up of sandstone rocks similar to those exposed on the cliff faces of Table Mountain.

Figure 7. A true-colour composite image of southern Africa from space, acquired by NASA's Aqua and Terra satellites on 7 November 2002.

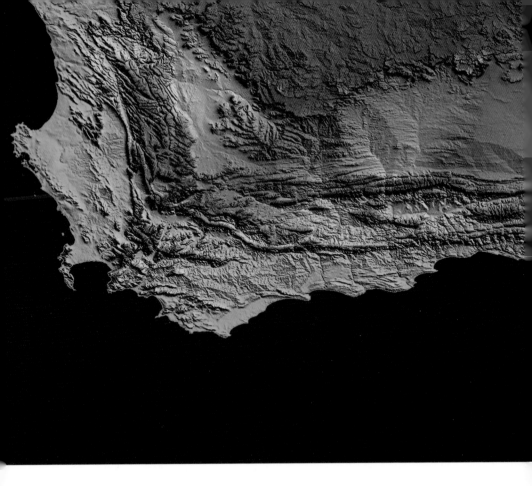

The distinct features of the South African coastline are also clearly visible when viewed from space and reveal that the Cape Peninsula is a pronounced but small part of a much larger, broader peninsula at the southwest tip of Africa. This larger peninsula coincides with the elbow-like kink in the Cape Fold Belt and contains, in addition to the mountains of the Cape Fold Belt, a series of granite hills scattered along a line that runs from Cape Agulhas in the southeast to St Helena Bay in the northwest (Fig. 8b).

An unusual feature of South Africa is that as you journey further inland and cross the mountains of the Cape Fold Belt, the land rises abruptly again onto the flat but elevated Karoo Plateau (Fig. 9). The Karoo Plateau sits 1 100 to 1 600 m above sea level and extends from the Great Escarpment (Fig. 10) across the country, with the highest elevations of 3 500 m being reached in the Drakensberg mountains of Lesotho.

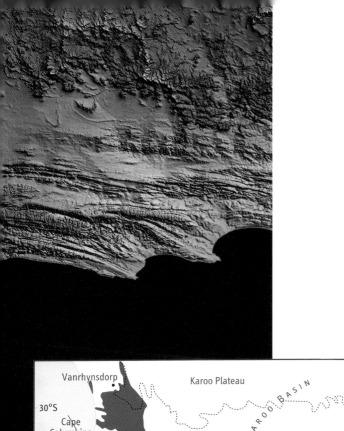

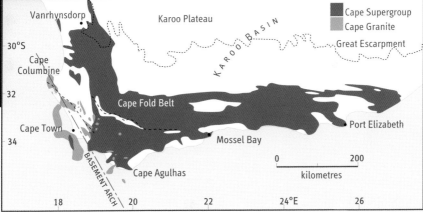

Figure 8.(a) (Above) An elevation map of southern Africa showing the land features captured in the satellite image.
(b) (Below) The Great Escarpment, the Cape Fold Belt and the linear array of granite hills that defines the Agulhas–Columbine Arch. This resistant feature forms the large peninsula on the southwest tip of Africa.

Figure 9. Cape Town sits on the edge of the African continent.
(Above) Features (vertically exaggerated) of the Cape Town area,
looking east into the Cape Fold Belt Mountains, taken from the
Landsat and Shuttle Radar Topography Mission.
(Below) The deep sea floor rises gradually and then rapidly up onto
the continental shelf. The shelf is the relatively flat offshore feature
that extends onto land as the coastal plain. The Cape Peninsula
mountains and granite hills rise abruptly from the coastal plain before
the spectacular rise of the Cape Fold Belt Mountains. The elevated
Karoo Plateau extends inland.

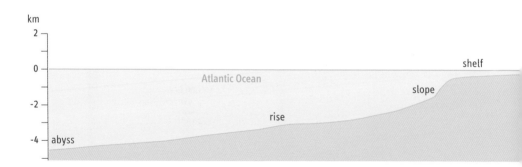

Figure 10. The Great Escarpment marks where the Karoo Plateau rises abruptly by over 1 000 m above the coastal plain, seen here at the town of Klawer and looking east from the N7, 20 km north of Vanrhynsdorp (inset).

CAPE FOLD BELT MOUNTAINS →

Table Mountain
Cape Town
Tygerberg
Paarl Rock
Bain's Kloof Pass
Michell's Pass
Ceres
Karoopoort
Great Escarpment
Sutherland

1:2 000 000
10x vertical exaggeration

20 km

PLATE TECTONICS

Plate tectonics is a general theory that explains many of Earth's dynamic features. Earth's crust – its thin, apple-skin outermost layer – can be divided into about a dozen large, rigid plates. These plates move in relation to one another in response to the plastic flow of rocks deep in Earth as heat is transferred from the hot interior to the surface (Fig. 11). Oceanic crust is continually being produced along the mid-oceanic ridge – a large mountain chain that runs for 80 000 km like a suture down the middle of the ocean basins. Magma rises up from the mantle as the ridge is pulled apart at a rate similar to that at which human fingernails grow. Because Earth is not expanding, the production of new crust at mid-ocean ridges requires destruction of old oceanic crust elsewhere. Old, cold and hence dense oceanic crust is destroyed by sinking back into the mantle along what are called subduction zones, demarcated on the surface by deep oceanic trenches and volcanoes. Continental crust consists of generally old, relatively thick accumulations of lighter rocks that ride on this conveyor-belt-like, convective motion of continually cycled oceanic crust. However, continental crust is too light to be returned to the mantle and remains at the surface as the 'scum of Earth', sometimes colliding and sticking together to form supercontinents or splitting apart into the separate continents of the present day. Earthquakes, volcanoes and mountain building are common features along new or collisional plate boundaries. Billions of years in the future, Earth will have cooled to a point when plate tectonics will come to a grinding halt.

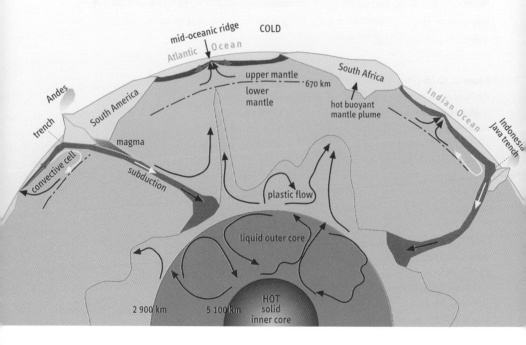

How did the extensive Cape Fold Belt, which includes the steep mountains surrounding Cape Town, form, and why is southern Africa so high? Mountains are created through powerful earth movements and are just one of many features that can be explained by plate tectonics (Fig. 11). Mountains represent areas of uplift, where enormous forces push large masses of rock upward against the force of gravity. One way in which such forces are generated is when two continents collide. The largest mountain range in the world, the Himalayas of Asia, formed when the Indian continent collided into the Asian continent – a collision that has been ongoing for the past 55 million years. A similar but ancient continental collision formed the Cape Fold Belt Mountains.

The collision ended over 200 million years ago and one would therefore expect southern Africa to have an old, low-lying, weathered surface similar to that of Australia. Why the mountains around Cape Town are so steep and the Karoo so high remain big and largely unanswered questions for earth scientists. One possible explanation is that deep below the surface a large plume of hot mantle rock – the African superswell – is ascending (Fig. 12). This plume is thought to have buoyed Africa up to make it the continent with the highest mean elevation (Fig. 13). In the south, the plume sustains the high elevations of the Karoo Plateau as well as the steep mountains of the Cape Fold Belt. To the north the plume expresses itself at the surface as the East African Rift Valley, floored by active volcanoes. As this plume continues its ascent, the East African Rift may extend into southern Africa and slowly, over many millions of years, split the African continent in two.

Figure 11. An idealised cut-away of the interior of Earth showing the 'lava-lamp' model of plate tectonics. At the centre of Earth is a solid iron-nickel core surrounded by a liquid outer core whose convection currents transfer heat to the core–mantle boundary (and produce Earth's magnetic field). Heated mantle rock rises plastically toward the surface and can cause continents to rise up and eventually split, as is believed to be happening under Africa currently. Relatively cold oceanic crust sinks back into the mantle at subduction zones to produce magma that ascends to form mountain belts like the Andes. Subduction also allows magma to ascend at the mid-oceanic ridges, where new oceanic crust is continually being produced. The lighter rocks of the continents forever ride on the surface, pushed apart or forced to collide with one another as oceanic crust is continually created and destroyed around them. Note that the crustal features are greatly exaggerated here.

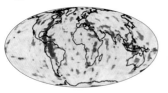
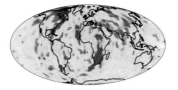
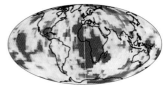

| 1 050 km | 1 800 km | 2 750 km |

Figure 12. A hot plume of mantle rock (red colour) rising 3 000
to 1 000 km below the African continent, imaged by changes
in the velocity of seismic waves generated during earthquakes
(seismic tomography).

It is these tectonic forces, far distant both in time and in space, that gave rise to
and sustain the landforms of Cape Town and the greater African continent. The uplift
of deeper rocks by tectonic forces is countered by the weathering away of the rocks at
the surface. In addition to tectonic forces, uplift occurs as the surface is weathered away
and new material rises from below to replace it. The reason for this additional uplift,
or isostatic adjustment, is similar to the reason for the movement of a boat in response
to people getting on or off: the continent will rise in areas where material has been
removed and sink in areas where material is added. However, isostasy alone cannot
sustain mountains indefinitely, just as an iceberg's height above the water will diminish
as it melts away. Without sustained uplift even the more resistant rocks are eventually
worn flat. In areas where tectonic uplift is ongoing, old, deeply buried rocks are eventually exhumed at the surface. For example, the granite rocks exposed in the Cape Town
area are estimated to have been 10 to 15 km below the surface around 600 million years
ago. The fact that we can see them at the surface now is testimony to a long period
of uplift and erosion. This feature is shared by most of the southern African surface,
which is made up of uplifted and eroded rocks; some, such as the Barberton Belt in
Mpumalanga, are as old as 3,5 billion years.

Therefore, Table Mountain rises dramatically above from the Cape Flats because
tectonic forces both ancient and recent have pushed it up. We have seen how the
landforms of Cape Town fit into the larger features of southern Africa, which in turn
have been shaped by the much larger global dynamics of plate tectonics. So much for
the big picture; now we need to come down to Earth and step up to the rock exposures
to focus on what they can tell us about how the diverse landscape of the Cape Town
area came about.

Figure 13. An elevation map of the African Plate, showing the overall high elevation of the African continent. Southern Africa rides passively on the African Plate, far from the active plate boundaries that are the mid-oceanic ridges of the South Atlantic, Southern Ocean and Indian Ocean, and the East African Rift Valley. As rifting continues, the East African Rift Valley may eventually be flooded by the sea, splitting the African continent in the same way that the Red Sea and the Gulf of Aden have split Arabia from Africa further to the north.

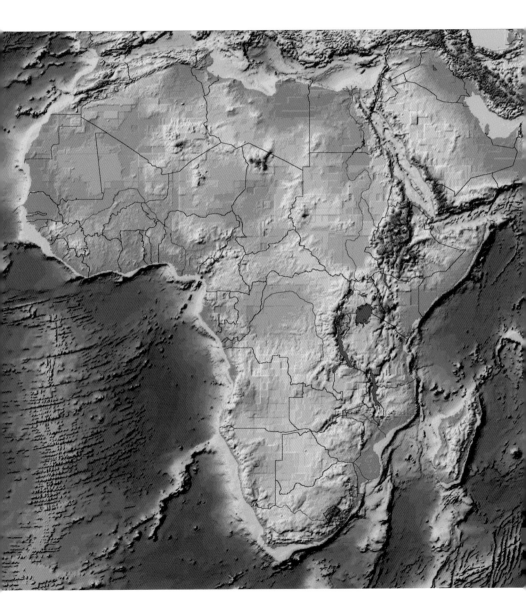

The Cape Town landscape can largely be understood through understanding the varying resistance of the underlying rocks as they are lifted up by large-scale tectonic forces and face the onslaught of weathering and erosion at the surface. For example, harder, more resistant granite and sandstone make up most of the hills and mountains surrounding Cape Town, whereas the relatively soft and easily worn-away shale tends to form low-lying areas such as the Cape Flats (Fig. 14). However, this simple assignment of rock type to landform doesn't always hold. For example, the Tygerberg hills and Signal Hill, which form steeply rounded and substantial features on the skyline, are composed of the same rock formation that underlies the CBD and the Cape Flats (Fig. 15). One possible explanation for their greater resistance is that the shale rocks of these hills were baked from below by hot magma, which now lurks out of sight beneath the surface as long-since-cooled granite.

You might also wonder why Table Mountain sits off on its own rather than as part of the larger, more continuous Cape Fold Belt Mountains that occur across the Cape Flats. The sand that makes up Table Mountain was deposited on the eroded surface of

a long-since-cooled granite. This means that hardening as a result of being baked from below by hot granite – which is used to explain the more resistant shale of Tygerberg and Blouberg – can be ruled out for the sandstone of Table Mountain. Rather, the answer may lie in the large-scale folding of these sandstone beds over the entire region, including where the Cape Flats are now, during the formation of the Cape Fold Belt. Over time, as the folded rocks were uplifted and eroded at the surface, the crests were worn away before the troughs of the folded rocks (Fig. 16). Once the crest of the folded sandstone was worn away, the underlying shale weathered more rapidly than the remaining sandstone trough that is now the prominent Table Mountain. Where did all these eroded rocks go? As we shall see, most ended up filling the basins located off-shore.

Table Mountain is cut by many gorges, which define prominent rock stacks, for example the Twelve Apostles above Camps Bay (Fig. 17) and Platteklip Gorge above the City Bowl (Fig. 18). The position of most of these gorges, including the larger-scale Noordhoek–Fish Hoek Valley, is related to faults or major joint sets in the rocks. Faults are planar surfaces that cut through large blocks of rocks across which the rocks on either side move in opposing directions. The amount of movement along most of these

Figure 14. The major underlying rock types that make up Cape Town's landscape. The solid white line depicts the contact between shale to the north and granite to the south. Sandstone makes up Table Mountain and Lion's Head. (Refer to the geological map, Fig. 80.)

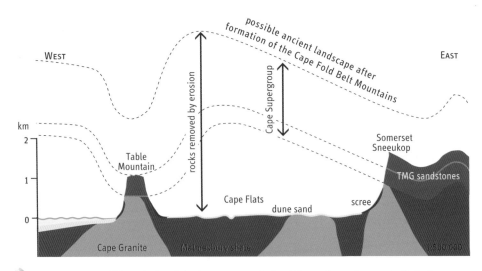

Figure 16. Possible evolution of the Cape Town landscape as depicted in this geological cross-section, which runs parallel to the N2 motorway out to Sir Lowry's Pass. The nearly flat-lying Table Mountain sandstones represent the trough (syncline) and the steeply dipping equivalent sandstones of the Hottentots Holland Mountains to the east the limb of a large fold that has since worn away to expose the underlying shale. Thus, the modern landscape may represent an inverted version of an earlier, ancient landscape (dashed lines) characterised by a large mountain where the Cape Flats are now.

Figure 15. (Above left) Looking down the Lion's back to Signal Hill at sunset. The surrounding flat areas of Green Point on the left and the CBD on the right, the sea floor under Table Bay, the distant hills of Blouberg (left) and Tygerberg (right) are all underlain by the same shale rock formation.

Figure 17. (Above right) The Twelve Apostles as seen from Camps Bay Beach were formed by erosion along fault planes that cut stream gorges into the large block of uplifted sandstone. The underlying granite is exposed on the beach in the foreground.

Figure 18. (Right) A sandstone cliff face along Platteklip Gorge, showing the intersecting fractures (joints) that form overhanging blocks, which will eventually cleave off and end up as large sandstone boulders on the lower mountain slopes.

nearly vertical fault planes is relatively small, but has provided a focal point for the run-off of rainwater. Focusing of runoff between the faulted blocks promotes erosion and the formation of the familiar steep valleys or gorges along which most of the major hiking trails run.

Large rounded granite boulders are another prominent feature seen on the slopes of granite hills such as Lion's Head and along the shore where granite is exposed, such as at Camps Bay and Boulders Beach (Fig. 19). Some granite boulders approach the size of a small house and look as if someone has sculpted them into an aesthetically pleasing rounded shape, not spherical or egg-shaped, but more like a bread roll. In some places granite boulders sit alone on a hillside; elsewhere they occur in clusters. The rounded shapes give the false impression that these granite boulders rolled into place from above. Although some of the smaller boulders may roll downhill or get tumbled in the surf, most granite boulders haven't moved at all.

How do these granite boulders form and why are they so distinct from the jagged, blocky exposures of sandstone and shale? For starters, granite is an igneous rock – in other words, it is crystallised from a liquid magma rather than deposited as sediment particles to form layers upon the sea floor. Granite therefore forms large, relatively homogeneous masses (blobs), in contrast to sediment, which forms stacks of successive flat-lying, cake-like layers of variable thickness and composition.

As rocks ascend toward the surface by uplift and the overlying rocks are eroded

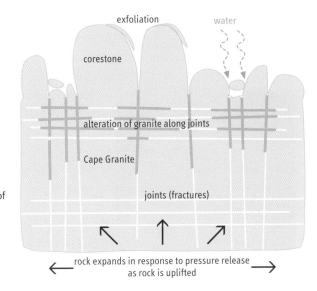

Figure 19. (Left) Granite at Boulders Beach, showing the round shape that results from the exfoliation of weathered layers.

Figure 20. (Right) The spacing of joints in granite bedrock varies and results in the formation of relatively large boulders (corestones) as weathering proceeds.

away, there is a release in pressure, which results in the expansion and fracturing of the rock along surfaces of relative weakness called joints. Joints in sandstone run in several different cross-cutting directions and are fairly close together. This produces the angular sandstone blocks notorious for falling onto mountain roads such as Chapman's Peak Drive. Shale joints are generally even finer and more closely spaced than those in sandstone. Joints in granite are far less uniform and tend to be spaced far apart (Fig. 20). Joints provide the pathways along which water first enters the rock, and weathering around the joints in turn promotes more fluid flow. By the time the granite makes it to the surface the altered, rotten granite along the joints is weathered away and the harder, unaltered granite between joints is left behind. Where the joints are relatively far apart, the granite blocks are large and consequently the last to weather out and form granite boulders. These boulders are referred to as corestones and they take on a rounded rather than a blocky shape because granite tends to weather by exfoliating the surface layer, like peeling off the successive layers of an onion.

Therefore, the rock types in general correspond to the landforms: sandstone forms tightly jointed blocky cliffs, granite forms rounded hills peppered with corestone boulders and shale forms low-lying flat areas – except where it is locally baked by granite or next to areas where it is capped by resistant sandstone. But what is it about these rocks that determines their resistance to weathering, and how then are they finally broken down to carve out the landscape we see around us?

Weathering removes rock and thereby limits the amount of uplift that occurs on land. Physical weathering breaks up rocks by forces such as the expansion of joints (just discussed), wedging by ice or plant roots, rockfalls and wind abrasion. The breaking up of rock into smaller pieces increases the surface area available to chemical weathering. Chemical weathering of rocks includes dissolving the rock in water as well as altering the rock by reaction with oxygen and acids in the water. Chemical weathering in turn makes it easier to break up the rock into even finer pieces. And so on it goes, with physical and chemical weathering continuing at the same time and reinforcing each other. The rate at which the surface weathers depends largely on the rock type and climate, with wet and warm conditions accelerating weathering. Higher-lying areas tend to take the brunt of weathering because they receive more rainfall and have greater temperature variations and steeper slopes that result in faster-flowing streams. In addition, wetter areas have more vegetation, which promotes weathering. These factors tend to limit the effect of different rock types on the development of landscapes.

Water is by far the most important weathering agent. It provides the medium in which chemical reactions can take place and carries away the salts and rock particles via rivers to the sea. Annual rainfall and hence the rate of erosion in the Cape Town area vary hugely from 2 000 mm at Newlands Forest to 600 mm at Sea Point and only 250 mm at Langebaan, 100 km up the West Coast. Water dissolves the minerals that make up rocks, with some minerals, such as halite (table salt), being highly soluble, and others, such as quartz, being only very slightly soluble in water. As the dissolved salt content of water increases, so too does its chemical reactivity, and this is why corrosion is so rapid in areas near the Cape coast where ocean spray carries with it large amounts of sea salt.

Figure 21. Soil forms from the weathering of rocks. Surface waters take up oxygen and carbon dioxide gases from the atmosphere and alter the minerals in rocks – for example, feldspar minerals change to the clay mineral kaolinite. Plants promote weathering because their dead organic material in soils decays to produce CO_2 – effectively, the photosynthesis reaction run in reverse. The acidic water also dissolves small amounts of iron and manganese in the sandstone as they flow through the cracks. When these waters eventually flow out of the mountain, the iron and manganese rapidly precipitate as oxide minerals when they are exposed to the oxygen-rich air (Fig. 22).

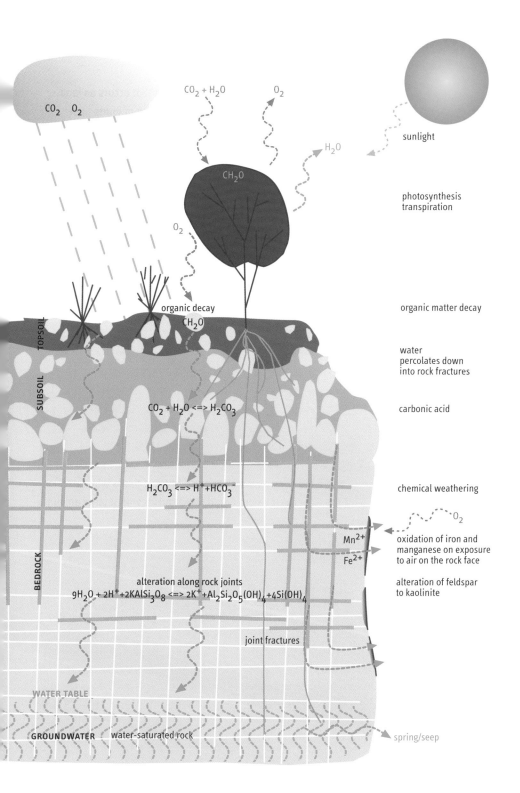

$CO_2 + H_2O$

O_2

sunlight

CH_2O

H_2O

photosynthesis
transpiration

CO_2 O_2

O_2

organic decay
CH_2O

organic matter decay

TOPSOIL

SUBSOIL

water
percolates down
into rock fractures

$CO_2 + H_2O \iff H_2CO_3$

carbonic acid

$H_2CO_3 \iff H^+ + HCO_3^-$

chemical weathering

O_2

Mn^{2+}

Fe^{2+}

oxidation of iron and
manganese on exposure
to air on the rock face

BEDROCK

alteration along rock joints
$9H_2O + 2H^+ + 2KAlSi_3O_8 \iff 2K^+ + Al_2Si_2O_5(OH)_4 + 4Si(OH)_4$

alteration of feldspar
to kaolinite

joint fractures

WATER TABLE

GROUNDWATER   water-saturated rock

spring/seep

Figure 22. An orange (iron) and black (manganese) stained sandstone above Hout Bay. The oxides commonly extend just millimetres below the surface of the greyish-white sandstone (inset).

In addition to dissolved salts, water carries dissolved carbon dioxide and oxygen gases, which it picks up from the atmosphere and soil (Fig. 21). Carbon dioxide forms an acid in water that attacks, for example, carbonate and feldspar minerals, while oxygen reacts with other minerals that contain iron, such as biotite. Weathering is generally a slow process but is visible on many of the rocks exposed in the Cape Town area. For example, the orange colour on the surface of many granite and sandstone rocks is a thin deposit of iron oxide (Fig. 22), which accumulates as a highly insoluble residue and which is not easily washed away. These same iron oxides are what give the common orange to reddish colour to soils and make up the rust that so rapidly forms on exposed steel surfaces.

Figure 23. Dark grey to black manganese oxides mined from Hout Bay.

In some areas of Table Mountain manganese oxide occurs as much more substantial deposits than surface coatings (Fig. 23). For example, a pocket of manganese ore was mined in the early 1900s above Hout Bay. The black ore was sent down chutes and loaded directly into ships in the bay; you can still see remnants of the mine shafts and ore-loading pier today. You can also see distinctive dark grey to black veins of manganese oxide in other areas of Table Mountain, for example, along the river on the Skeleton Gorge trail above Kirstenbosch Botanical Gardens. Manganese oxide can form crystals along thin fractures in the rock. The fernleaf-like patterns of these crystals make them easily mistaken for plant fossils.

In places where the weathered granite has not washed away, you can literally crumble the once rock-hard granite in your hands. This rotten, crumbly granite is exposed in road cuts all along the Cape Peninsula and is a concern to engineers building on the granite (Fig. 24). The reason you can crumble it is that the large, white, blocky feldspar crystals that make up well over half the granite have altered to kaolinite, a soft white clay mineral that leaves a talcum-powder-like residue on your hands. On the Cape Peninsula there are several deep pockets of weathered granite that are mined for kaolinite used in making ceramics and glossy paper. These kaolinite deposits are believed to have formed tens of millions of years ago when the Cape had a warmer and wetter climate, which promoted deep weathering of the granite.

Although shale underlies much of the Cape Flats, finding fresh exposures of it is difficult because it weathers rapidly. The reason for this is that, in addition to its many fine cracks (joints), shale is composed of fine-grained minerals, which are attacked by the acid and oxygen carried by surface waters. Dark, fresh exposures of shale can be seen where it is actively eroded and exposed, such as along the coast at Sea Point; but where it has been exposed for a longer time, for example, high on Mowbray Ridge, it is a leached yellow-orange colour and crumbles easily in your hands (Fig. 25).

In contrast, the sandstone of Table Mountain is made up almost entirely of quartz – a mineral largely impervious to the acids and oxygen of surface waters, which so readily attack shale and granite. In fact, the lack of reaction with quartz results in the acid waters draining Table Mountain. Mountain streams have a pH of 4, making them more than ten times as acidic as rainwater, which has a pH of 5,6. These acid-charged waters then chemically attack the underlying down-slope shale or granite, making the sandstone cliffs above even more prominent. Water that percolates through the fractured sandstone beds carries, in addition to iron and manganese, small amounts of dissolved quartz. The quartz then precipitates out as this water evaporates after seeping out onto the sandstone cliff faces. If you look closely, you can often see the sparkling faces of

Figure 24. Erosion of rotten granite along the roadside opposite Third Beach at Clifton. A large corestone is visible on the right.

small hexagonal (six-sided) quartz crystals on the sandstone surfaces. This additional quartz surface cement makes the sandstone even harder and more resistant to weathering and further promotes the formation of sandstone cliffs. The erosion of the sandstone therefore relies largely on the collapse of the sandstone cliffs under the force of gravity, as you can see from the strewn sandstone blocks scattered below them.

In conclusion, the highs and lows of the landscape that form on this tectonically raised surface largely reflect the variable susceptibility of the different underlying rocks to weathering. The hard and chemically inert quartz-rich sandstone weathers much more slowly than granite, which in turn weathers more slowly than shale. The greater mineral variety of granite and shale makes them far more reactive than the sandstone to acids and oxygen carried by surface waters. These chemical reactions allow granite and shale to develop deeper and more nutrient-rich soils than the sandstone, and have a large influence on the type of vegetation that the different rock types can support.

Figure 25. A typical shallow soil profile of mountain fynbos exposed on Mowbray Ridge. Highly weathered, finely jointed shale beds can be seen dipping to the right.

Rocks have a major influence on the plants that grow above them, mostly because they determine the types of soil that form, which in turn largely determines the types of plants that can grow in different areas. The interaction between plants and rocks is a powerful one, because plants accelerate rock weathering and the formation of soils beneficial to plants, but slow down physical erosion of the soil. For example, the weathering of feldspar to kaolinite releases ions such as potassium that are needed by plants. The first plants to colonise bare rock surfaces are lichens, a mutually beneficial (symbiotic) mixture of algae and fungi whose multicoloured circular to patchy forms are common, along with the iron and manganese oxides just discussed, on rock surfaces in the Cape (Fig. 26). Lichens hold water and produce organic acids which promote the breakdown of rock to soil. Soil is essential for the larger plants that are commonly found growing in the nearby crevices of joint fractures in the rocks.

Figure 26. Circular patches of lichens growing on the exposed surfaces of fallen sandstone blocks. The amount of time since the rock fell can be estimated if the growth rate of the lichens is known (lichenometry).

Much of the vegetation we see today is different from the indigenous plants that originally grew in the Cape Town area. The difference is greatest in the low-lying areas of the Cape Flats and on arable land, and many of these areas are now dominated by alien rather than indigenous plants. The limited numbers of large trees, such as those preserved in Skeleton Gorge above the Kirstenbosch Botanical Gardens, led European settlers to plant pine plantations, in part perhaps from a longing for their familiar forests, but more practically as a source of fuel and timber.

The low-lying Cape Flats have suffered the greatest impact from the displacement of vegetation by farming, buildings and roads. Europeans stabilised the large mobile sand dunes, which travel quickly on the strong southeast wind, by the planting of Australian acacias from the middle of the 19th century. These plants had the desired effect of trapping annoying wind-blown sand, but have since successfully invaded and displaced many nearby plant communities.

Many of the coastal areas are covered by wind-blown beach sands that support strandveld vegetation. Strandveld vegetation manages to produce a diverse flora adapted to moving sand. Because the sandy soil contains anywhere from 5 to 95 percent calcareous shell fragments and receives moisture from coastal fog as well as salts from sea spray, it can support fruiting bushes whose berries help sustain insects and birds. In older deposits of wind-blown sand the calcareous shell can be removed entirely by acidic rainwaters to produce nearly pure (99,68 percent SiO_2), well-sorted fine quartz sands. In the Philippi area these sands are mined for making glass.

Away from the coastal areas, where there is no dune sand cover, the weathering of the more diverse minerals in the underlying shale rocks produces dark, clayey, nutrient-rich soils. Patches of the indigenous renosterveld vegetation typical of these fertile soils exist on Signal Hill but are now largely replaced by grasses. Renosterveld once extended over much of the lowlands along the West Coast north of Cape Town – the Swartland – which are now almost completely replaced by winter wheat.

The mountain fynbos has fared better, protected from development by steep and rocky slopes (Fig. 27). A number of nature reserves have been established – such as Kogelberg and Orange Kloof in the Table Mountain National Park – to protect the diverse Cape floral ecosystem. The fynbos consists of a remarkably diverse assemblage of heathers (ericas), reeds (restios), large bushes (proteas) and bulbs (geophytes), many of which are endemic and found nowhere else except in the Western Cape. Soils, particularly on the steep sandstone slopes of Table Mountain, are generally nutrient-poor (as they are on the wind-blown, sand-covered Cape Flats), being derived from rock almost exclusively made up of quartz sand with a simple and not very nutritious composition of silicon dioxide (SiO_2).

In addition to being nutrient-poor, many of the mountain soils are shallow, with only a few centimetres of sandy soil resting on bedrock (Fig. 25). Fynbos plants are adapted to low-nutrient soils in being able to retain what nutrients come their way in the form of sea salts transported by wind and rain, as well as in ash deposited after fire or in Karoo dust delivered by Berg wind events, which supply potassium and calcium to the plants. Fynbos is also adapted to strong seasonal rainfall and the dry summers by having tough, waxy (sclerophyllous) leaves. The plants are adapted to fire, with some seeds germinating on cue from the aromatic chemicals of smoke, which alert them to the boom in available space and nutrients that follows fire.

We have seen how the varied landscape and its vegetation are largely the result of large-scale and long-term tectonic forces as well as weathering of the different rock types at the surface. Weathering of the uplifted surface has sculpted the land into hard, chemically-resistant, sandstone cliff-faced mountains such as Table Mountain; rounded granite hills whose slopes are scattered with granite corestone boulders; and arable flat lands underlain by the more easily weathered shale rock.

We can now answer the question posed at the beginning of this chapter: Table Mountain is an eroded remnant of resistant sandstone rock, as well as a block of rock that was pushed up by an earlier continental collision – and one that appears to con-tinue to be pushed up by the dynamics of the deep Earth. The combination of these two factors – uplift and variable resistance to erosion – has produced the surface features we observe today. The soils produced during the weathering of these rocks range from thin, nutrient-poor quartz-rich soils on the mountains to deep, fertile clayey soils in the low-lying areas not covered by wind-blown sand. And the variation in vegetation gener-ally reflects the adaptation of plants to these soil differences.

But the landscape and its features that we observe today are simply the latest chapter in a long and complex history. What can the rocks surrounding Cape Town tell us of the region's far-deeper geological history?

Figure 27. Mountain fynbos above Chapman's Peak Drive. Protea bushes, fine-leafed ericas and reedy restios can be seen on the boulder-strewn slope in the foreground.

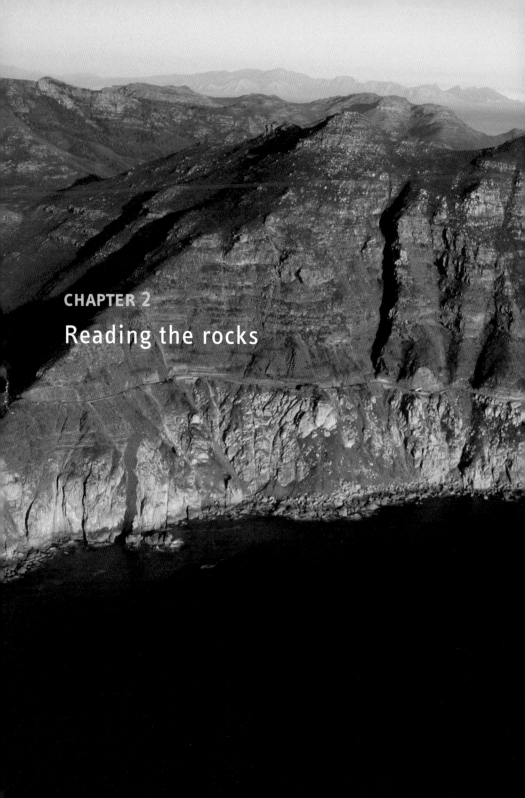

CHAPTER 2

Reading the rocks

Figure 28. The rock stack exposed along the cliff face of Chapman's Peak Drive provides a record of Cape Town's deep geological history.

In the previous chapter, we saw that rocks have a large influence on the landscape, soil and vegetation in the Cape Town area. In addition to this relatively recent imprint, the rocks of Cape Town have their own far more ancient origins. What we see today (Fig. 28) is the end product of a long history of geological events and processes that have operated over vast distances and for millions of years. The rocks reveal a wide spectrum of vastly different environments, ranging from subtropical beaches to polar ice caps. These environments have evolved over the long eras of geologic time in the vicinity of what we know today as Cape Town. The story the rocks tell is often difficult to grasp because we are not accustomed to thinking about our world over such enormous spans of time, living as we do from day to day, year to year.

Geologic time is sometimes referred to as deep time, for it reaches back millions – even billions – of years into the past. The raising up of mountains and the opening of ocean basins take millions of years at the rate Earth moves. Most geologic change is imperceptibly slow to us until the ground shakes under our feet during an earthquake. How can we comprehend deep time? A commonly used device is to compress the 4,6 billion years of Earth history into the space of one calendar year. On the first of January our Earth and solar system form; by mid-February the oldest rocks yet discovered form on the surface, and by late March some include simple, unicellular life; it is not until 22 November that abundant multicellular life arrives on the scene; on Christmas Day Earth is struck by a large asteroid and the dinosaurs become extinct; by late morning on New Year's Eve our oldest hominid ancestors break away from the apes; and finally modern humans arrive at around 20 minutes before midnight.

Rocks provide our window into the deep past. We shall see that in the Cape Town area, as elsewhere, only a very incomplete and partial record of Earth history is on offer: most of time is not represented at all except as large gaps in the rock record. These gaps occur because rocks are continually being recycled as a result of plate tectonics (Fig. 29). Gaps in the rocks represent periods during which the surface in the Cape Town area was undergoing erosion rather than accumulation. Even during those periods when rocks manage to accumulate, only a small fraction of the environment of which they are a part is captured, with most living organisms unlikely to be preserved as fossils and the gases of the atmosphere or water surrounding them even less so. Therefore, the task of reading the rocks becomes paramount to our understanding of the past. Although they are not ideal recorders, they are all we have.

What follows is a reading of the story that rocks exposed in the greater Cape Town area have to tell, so that the next time you see them up close or from a distance you will recognise them as being more than 'just rocks'. The story of the rocks is told from oldest to youngest – not out of respect for age, but because it gives the correct order in which events occurred, from the deep past right on through to the present day.

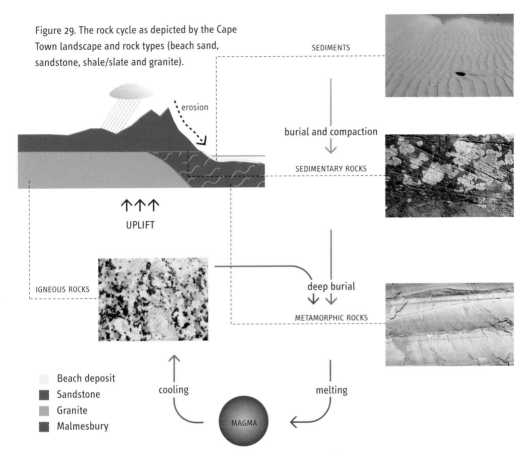

Figure 29. The rock cycle as depicted by the Cape Town landscape and rock types (beach sand, sandstone, shale/slate and granite).

SEDIMENTS

erosion

burial and compaction

SEDIMENTARY ROCKS

UPLIFT

IGNEOUS ROCKS

deep burial

METAMORPHIC ROCKS

Beach deposit
Sandstone
Granite
Malmesbury

cooling

MAGMA

melting

THE ROCK CYCLE

Rocks are divided into three types: sedimentary, metamorphic and igneous. All three are represented in the Cape Town area and examples of each are shown here. The rocks that make up Earth are dynamic (Fig. 11) and are continually being transformed, either by deep burial or by uplift and weathering, from one rock type to another (Fig. 29). Sedimentary rocks are first deposited as loose sediment particles derived from the breakdown of pre-existing rocks or from the formation of new particles from salts dissolved in water. A common type of sediment is beach sand, which in the Cape Town area consists of roughly equal proportions of quartz grains (weathered from the rocks of Table Mountain) and shell fragments. Compaction and cementation by deep burial transforms sand into sandstone. Similarly, mud is buried to form mudstone, which upon deeper burial transforms into shale and then slate (sometimes used as roof tiles) in response to increasing pressure and temperature. At sufficiently high temperatures and pressures, minerals transform into new minerals that give a shiny sheen to metamorphic rocks, and at great depths the rock melts to form a liquid magma. Igneous rocks form from magma – coarsely crystalline if the magma cools slowly, and finely crystalline or glassy if the magma cools rapidly in a volcanic eruption. The cycle is completed by the eventual uplift of all three rock types to the surface, where they weather to form new sediment deposits.

The oldest rocks in the Cape Town area were originally deposited as marine mud and muddy sands, which today make up a suite of rocks known as the Malmesbury Group. These were named, as is often the case, after the area where they were first or most completely described – in this case, near the town of Malmesbury in the Swartland north of Cape Town (Fig. 1). The Malmesbury Group a comprises diverse set of rocks that is dominated in the Cape Town area by shale (metamorphosed mud) and greywacke (muddy sands). Malmesbury rocks are widespread in the Cape Town area, underlying much of the coastal plain (CBD, Cape Flats, Swartland) as well as Signal Hill, Mowbray Ridge and the hills of the Tygerberg. However, unaltered exposures are rare because these fine-grained, highly fractured rocks weather relatively quickly and are covered by soil or wind-blown sand in most areas.

You can see relatively fresh (unaltered), dark-coloured Malmesbury rocks exceptionally well exposed all along the Promenade at Sea Point (Fig. 30). Although they have since been folded and buried into hard rocks, many features acquired when the sediment first accumulated on the sea floor as soft mud are preserved and provide clues to the environment in which Malmesbury rocks were deposited. Many features of these rocks – such as ripples – are similar to those found in sediments today (Fig. 31).

But there are two significant and linked differences between the ancient Malmesbury rocks and modern sediment: Malmesbury rocks lack fossils and have abundant fine depositional layers called laminations (Fig. 32). Laminations are rare in modern sediment because animals (mostly worms) living on the sea floor or in soil are constantly ingesting and burrowing through the sediment. The effect over time is a homogeneous, well-mixed sediment with no fine layers of deposition preserved. The reason Malmesbury rocks are laminated and lack fossil animals is that sea-bed animals

Figure 30. Erosion by powerful surf exposes Malmesbury rocks along the Sea Point Promenade. The rock layers extend offshore to the northwest, steeply dipping to the northeast, with mud-rich shale layers forming gullies and sand-rich layers (greywacke) forming more resistant ridges. These rocks form part of the wave-cut terrace upon which Sea Point is built. The over 300 m high ridge in the background is made up of Malmesbury rocks as well as granite underneath Lion's Head on the right. The Cableway Station is visible on top of Table Mountain on the distant skyline.

Figure 31. A comparison of modern sand ripples moving along the bed of the Disa River where it empties into Hout Bay (left) and ancient ripples preserved in muddy sandstones of the Table Mountain Group exposed above Hout Bay on Chapman's Peak Drive (below).

THE PRESENT IS THE KEY TO THE PAST

One of the most powerful approaches to deciphering the story of ancient rocks is to find modern examples where similar rocks are actively forming today. The principle of uniformitarianism, championed by one of the founding fathers of geology, Charles Lyell, is summed up by the statement: 'The present is the key to the past.' The idea is that what we observe today also happened in the past and that the cumulative, long-term effect can be seen in the rock record: for example, how ripples are formed in sand by flowing water (Fig. 31). One limitation of uniformitarianism is that conditions on Earth have not always been the same as today. The climate as well as the composition of the atmosphere and seawater have changed over time; and for much of Earth history, life on the planet consisted of single-celled organisms (until November on our compressed calendar). We have witnessed only a wink of the eye of Earth history, and many past events and environments are not represented on Earth today. Although uniformitarianism is an extremely powerful tool to interpret the rock record, one should always bear in mind that many aspects of the past were significantly different from the present.

Figure 32. Close inspection of Malmesbury rocks at Van Riebeeck's Quarry on Robben Island and in a Sea Point tidal pool reveals the presence of fine (less than 1 cm thick) sediment layers called laminations.

with hard skeletons had not yet evolved on Earth in significant numbers at the time when these rocks were forming. The dark colours of Malmesbury rocks indicate that there is organic matter in the sediment, but it takes the form of the remains of single-celled bacteria and algae. Unlike animals, these small organisms were incapable of disrupting fine sediment layers and more likely carpeted the seafloor in mats of algae that helped to preserve the laminated sediment.

Graded bedding can also commonly be seen in Malmesbury rocks. Graded beds contain what are referred to as turbidite deposits. These form from the settling out of sediment that has been suspended by large-scale slumping events, often triggered by an earthquake. As the sediment grains settle out of the turbid water, the larger grains reach the bottom first, followed by finer grains. Ripples and graded bedding provide important indicators as to the 'right way up' in sedimentary rocks like these, which have been intensely folded.

In addition to sedimentary rocks, the Malmesbury Group contains volcanic rocks, which tell us volcanoes were active at least episodically during their deposition. You can see these reddish-brown volcanic rocks along the rocky shores at Bloubergstrand. The presence of volcanic rocks is revealing for, unlike the modern offshore sediments, these

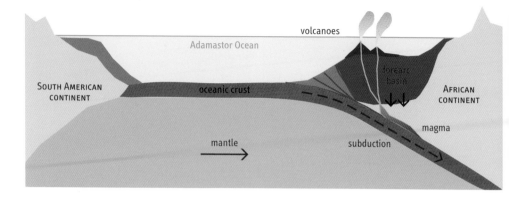

Figure 33. Possible tectonic setting during deposition of the Malmesbury Group.

earlier sediments most likely accumulated on a tectonically active margin with volcanoes being generated as oceanic crust was subducted below the continent (Fig. 33).

We know that Malmesbury rocks are the oldest in the Cape Town area because they always occur at the lowest levels and all other rocks either rest on top of or cross-cut Malmesbury rocks. But how long ago were Malmesbury rocks deposited? This is not an easy question to answer, in large part because these rocks lack fossils. The youngest of a number of individually dated (Fig. 34) grains of zircon (a hard-wearing and hence common trace mineral found in sedimentary rocks) reveals that Malmesbury rocks sampled at Sea Point are no older than 560 million years. This may not appear to be very helpful except that, as we shall see, the granite that intrudes Malmesbury rocks is about 540 million years old. Therefore, Malmesbury sediments were deposited some time between 560 and 540 million years ago.

In summary, Malmesbury rocks are the oldest in the Cape Town area, having originally accumulated some time between 560 and 540 million years ago as muddy sediment on the edge of a tectonically active continent. The fine laminations and absence of fossils indicate that these sediments accumulated before there were abundant animals on Earth. It is not known how deeply the Malmesbury rocks extend because no one has ever drilled to the older rocks beneath them. However, they are believed to represent a thick pile of sediment similar to the wedge of sediment up to 18 km thick that sits on the present-day edge of the continent deposited since Africa split away from South America 135 million years ago. The history of plate tectonics tells us that Malmesbury sediment did not accumulate on the edge of the present-day South Atlantic Ocean basin, but in an earlier ocean basin called Adamastor.

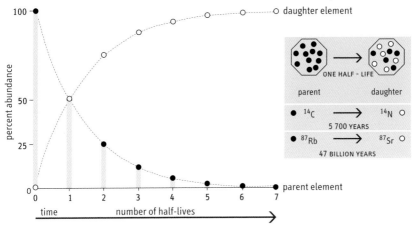

Figure 34. A determination of the absolute age of rocks relies on the fact that some elements (the parent) spontaneously decay to stable (daughter) elements. If certain conditions are met, then the relative abundance of parent and daughter elements can be used to determine how many years ago the mineral formed.

The rate of decay varies among radioactive elements. For example, carbon atoms with an atomic mass of 14 are radioactive, as are rubidium atoms of atomic mass 87, but the time required for half of the carbon 14 atoms to decay (half-life) is approximately 5 700 years and 47 billion years for rubidium 87. For this reason, carbon 14 is used to date relatively recent material (<50 000 years old) and rubidium 87 is used to date older rocks (>500 million years).

DATING ROCKS, RELATIVELY AND ABSOLUTELY

Determining the relative age of rocks is fairly straightforward. For example, because sediment is deposited as nearly flat layers (the principle of original horizontality), the rocks at the top of a stack of sediment layers must be younger than the rocks below (the principle of superposition). Where sediment layers have been tilted or turned upside down by folding, features of the sediment – such as ripples, graded bedding or cross-bedding – can be used to determine the original way up. But stacks of sediment vary from place to place and reflect the wide variety of different types of sediment that accumulate on the surface at any given time. This variation makes it difficult to correlate rocks unless they contain fossils. Rocks containing the same fossils were deposited within the interval of time when those organisms lived. Because extinction is forever and the evolutionary turnover of new species is quite rapid on geological timescales (the average species exists for 4 million years), fossils are useful in correlating similarly aged rocks.

Although relative ages are useful, they give only a crude history of the rocks. Geologists want to know exactly how many years ago a particular rock formed. Radioactivity, the spontaneous decay of one element into another, is commonly used to assign an absolute or numerical age to a rock. Igneous rocks are typically the best candidates for absolute dating because many of the radioactive clocks start when minerals first crystallise from the magma. For this reason the age of the Cape Granite is much better known than that of the sedimentary Malmesbury rocks (no one has yet dated the Malmesbury volcanic rocks at Bloubergstrand).

The next major event – revealed by the prominent granite hills of Lion's Head and Paarl Rock and the large rounded granite boulders exposed along much of the Cape Peninsula shoreline (Fig. 19) – was the intrusion of the Cape Granite magma into the underbelly of the Malmesbury rocks. This magma is thought to have originated at depth below the continent from the partial melting of old, dense oceanic crust as it sank back (subducted) into the mantle. The ancient ocean basin of Adamastor closed as the African continent approached and eventually collided with the South American and Antarctic continents (Fig. 35). The magma coalesced into subsurface blobs that rose up buoyantly toward the surface, partially melting deep continental rocks along the way. The rising magma eventually intruded into and displaced the thick wedge of Malmesbury rocks as they were accumulating on the edge of the continent. The magma began to cool and crystallise at approximately 10 km below the surface into the granite rocks that we see today exposed on the surface. Granite hills extend from Cape Agulhas north to Cape Columbine (Fig. 8b) in a more or less linear array, made up of a variety of different igneous rock types referred to collectively as the Cape Granite Suite. The most common variety of granite in the Cape Town area is remarkable for its large white blocky feldspar crystals (Fig. 36).

In addition to pushing aside and folding Malmesbury rocks, the magma introduced

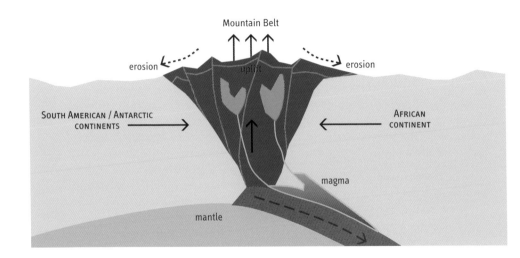

a great deal of heat. As the hot (900°C) magma was set in place, much of its heat was transferred to the surrounding Malmesbury rocks, which at 10 km depth would have had a much lower ambient temperature of around 250°C. The heat baked and recrystallised the Malmesbury shale locally to a metamorphic rock called hornfels. The heating was greatest where the magma was in direct contact with the Malmesbury rocks (Fig. 37), because rocks are generally poor conductors of heat. Black pieces of foreign rock (xenoliths), 5 to 100 cm across, are conspicuous in the granite rock (Fig. 38). Most of these are fragments of Malmesbury sedimentary rock, ripped up and carried by the force of the ascending magma.

Therefore, intrusion of the granite marks the beginning of a major tectonic reorganisation of the African continent. It took less than 20 million years (from 560 to 540 million years ago) for the Malmesbury rocks to be deposited and buried to a depth of 10 km. During this 20 million year period before the granite intrusion, the edge of the continent was subsiding, and this allowed Malmesbury sediment to accumulate, perhaps in a basin created by the subducting oceanic crust (Fig. 33). As subduction continued, the South American and Antarctic continents converged on Africa, effectively closing the ancient Adamastor Ocean basin between them. Subduction resulted in magma generation at deep levels, which rose to within 10 km of the surface to intrude and fold Malmesbury rocks. It is the intrusion of Cape Granite that marks the end of subsidence and the beginning of uplift and erosion in the Cape Town area.

Figure 35. Granitic magma rose up into the Malmesbury rocks as the ancient ocean basin of Adamastor closed up and the South American and Antarctic continents started to collide with Africa. The collision resulted in deformation and uplift of the deep granite-intruded Malmesbury rocks, until erosion eventually exposed these rocks at the surface.

THE SEA POINT CONTACT

At the Sea Point Contact you can inspect a spectacular freeze-frame image of the contact between hot magma and Malmesbury rocks that occurred over 500 million years ago, 10 km below the surface of Earth (Fig. 37). This complex contact is beautifully exposed on the wave-eroded coast and is easily accessed from the Bantry Bay parking lot, its location below the sea wall marked by a plaque proclaiming its geological importance. For geologists of the early 19th century, this exposure raised a host of very basic questions about the meaning of rocks and compelled Charles Darwin to describe it during his visit to the Cape

in 1836 on the HMS 'Beagle'. The impact of the magma on the surrounding Malmesbury rocks fades away from the contact to the north to form a halo of heat alteration called a contact aureole. The complex interface between the granite intrusion and the Malmesbury rocks can be traced from the Sea Point Contact up the side of Lion's Head, where it forms the base of the neck of the lion; it then cuts across the upper reaches of the City Bowl and extends under the saddle between Table Mountain and Devil's Peak, to the other side near Wynberg Hill; and finally it continues out into False Bay (Fig. 14).

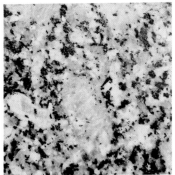

Figure 36. A polished slab of Cape Granite, showing the large white blocky feldspar crystals (megacrysts), some 4 to 6 cm across. These crystals testify to the slow rate at which the magma cooled. In addition to large feldspar crystals, the granite contains translucent, grey quartz and black biotite crystals.

Figure 37. The Sea Point Contact exposed on the shore at Bantry Bay, with the dark-baked Malmesbury rocks on the lower left and the light-coloured granite on the upper right. This picture captures only part of a much more extensive zone of complex mixing of igneous and sedimentary rocks.

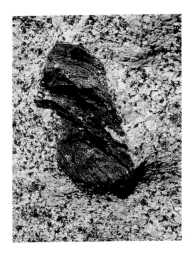

Figure 38. A fragment of Malmesbury rock (xenolith) floating in a granite exposure at Boulders Beach. The original sediment layers can be seen, but this Malmesbury rock has taken on a dark, coarsely crystalline texture as a result of direct heating, with some of the rock melting into the surrounding granite magma and the remainder recrystallising into a hornfels metamorphic rock. You can often see xenoliths in Cape Granite. They clearly show the significant interaction that took place between the magma and the surrounding rocks during the magma's ascent toward the surface.

FLAT-LYING SANDSTONE

TILTED MALMESBURY

EROSIONAL CONTACT

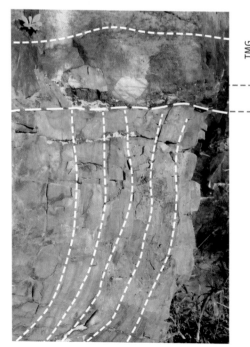

TMG SANDSTONE

MALMESBURY SHALE

Figure 39.(a) (Above) The contact between steeply dipping Malmesbury shale and relatively flat-lying TMG sandstone is called an angular unconformity because the two sedimentary layers, rather than being stacked one atop another like the pages in a book, are at an angle to one another.

(Left) A close-up view of the erosional contact between nearly vertical-dipping Malmesbury shales and flat-lying TMG sandstones with a white, rounded quartz cobble above the contact.

What happened after the intrusion and cooling of the granite had finished by around 540 million years ago? If we look to the rocks on display in Cape Town, we see that the Malmesbury and granite rocks are covered by mudstones and sandstones of the Table Mountain Group (TMG). The contact or boundary between the Malmesbury and TMG rocks is well exposed at the waterfall site along Tafelberg Road, and the contact between the granite and TMG rocks is well exposed at the southern end of Chapman's Peak Drive (Fig. 39). The contacts are striking because of the strong discontinuity in the type and orientation of the rocks on either side of them. The rocks below the contact are either steeply dipping Malmesbury rocks or granite and the rocks above are the nearly

Figure 39 (b). The contact between the granite and the TMG sandstone is called a nonconformity because granite, a deeply intruded igneous rock, is overlain by a sandstone deposited near sea level.

SANDSTONE LAYERS

WEATHERED GRANITE

FRESH GRANITE

flat-lying sandstones of the Table Mountain Group. In addition, the contacts are clearly erosional, marked by weathered and fragmented surfaces. These contacts represent a gap or hiatus in the rock record.

We can determine the amount of time 'missing' by this gap in the rocks if we know the age of the overlying sandstones. But like the Malmesbury rocks, the overlying TMG sandstones are difficult to date. The TMG, unlike the Malmesbury Group, was deposited after the widespread appearance of animals whose bodies contained hard parts that fossilised easily (like trilobites and brachiopods). But unfortunately only trace fossils have yet been found preserved in the lower TMG and these consist of small animal tracks. These trace fossils suggest an age of around 500 million years. Together with the age of the youngest zircon grains of around 510–518 million years, they indicate that the lower TMG sandstones were deposited 510 to 500 million years ago. So the difference between the age of the granite intrusion at 540 million years and the overlying TMG sandstones implies that the boundary represents a gap of 30 to 40 million years.

How did it come about that Malmesbury rocks, which had been descending to depths of around 10 km over the previous 20 million years (560 to 540 million years ago), were exposed at the surface and covered by coastal sands in the following 30 to 40 million years (510 to 500 million years ago)? Such a radical reversal in tectonic forces along the continental margin is explained by the head-on collision of two continents (Fig. 35).

This ancient collision is part of what geologists call the Pan African Event, which involved a series of continental collisions that formed the proto-supercontinent Gondwana: an amalgamation of South America, Africa, India, Antarctica and Australia. You can appreciate the result of two continents colliding if you consider the ongoing col-lision between the Indian and Asian continents, which continues to give rise to the large Himalayan-Tibetan Plateau although it began 50 million years ago.

It is in the tremendous forces of such grinding, melting, thrusting collisions that continents are soldered together. Similar to what we observe in the Himalayas today, continental pile-ups result in the uplift and erosion of huge amounts of crustal rocks, thrusting marine limestone, which was originally deposited below sea level, to the over 8 800 m high summit of Mount Everest and exposing deep crustal rocks at the surface. Therefore, continental collisions of the Pan African Event appear to have provided the force necessary to expose the deeply buried Malmesbury and granite rocks at the surface in the space of less than 40 million years. This major period of upheaval is displayed for us in the sharp discontinuity between the underlying Malmesbury and granite and overlying TMG rocks on the Cape Peninsula.

An enormous pile of sand

On top of this eroded, flat surface (called a peneplain) that cuts across Malmesbury and granite bedrock rests an enormous pile of sand (Fig. 40). Over 7 km thick, this pile of sand (which also includes intervals of mud) was deposited between 510 and 340 million years ago and is known as the Cape Supergroup (Fig. 41). It is the lowermost portion of

Figure 40. The transition from the maroon Graafwater Formation mudstones and sandstones to the overlying cliff-forming Peninsula Formation sandstone beds, exposed along the Platteklip Gorge trail, forms the base of the Cape Supergroup pile of sand.

this pile of sand that is exposed in the 600 m high sandstone cliffs of Table Mountain. The rest of the rocks that make up the Cape Supergroup can be found in the Cape Fold Belt Mountains.

Beautiful exposures of the approximately 70 m thick sandstones and distinctively maroon-coloured mudstones of the Graafwater Formation can be viewed along Chapman's Peak Drive, Tafelberg Road and the Contour Path that continues around to the King's Blockhouse. These roads and the Contour Path run just above the contact with the underlying granite or Malmesbury shale. The contact is usually covered by rock scree (talus), but the more resistant overlying Graafwater rocks are clearly marked by an increase in slope angle. The maroon mudstones and buff-coloured sandstones of the Graafwater are stacked in a cyclic pattern. The base of each cycle is dominated by sandstone, which is overlain by increasingly abundant mudstone layers, and these are in turn capped once again by sandstone layers (Fig. 42).

The Graafwater rocks (Fig. 43) are typical of sediment deposited on land where the abundance of oxygen in the atmosphere oxidises the iron to give a maroon-red rust colour to the sediment. In contrast to these so called 'terrestrial red beds', are the typically grey/black or green colour of marine muds, like the underlying Malmesbury shale, whose iron was not exposed to oxygen except where it was later weathered to form soil. If you look carefully, you can see a number of features displayed by Graafwater rocks, such as sand-filled desiccation cracks, which, along with their red colour, indicate at least intermittent exposure to air (Fig. 44). Another common feature seen throughout the entire Cape Supergroup rocks is cross-bedding (Fig. 45).

Figure 41. An idealised vertical stack of the rocks that make up the more than 7 km thick pile of sand in the Western Cape called the Cape Supergroup. The Cape Supergroup is subdivided into groups, which are further divided into formations (Fm) of similar rocks. Rocks in the Cape Town area belong to the lowermost Cape Supergroup and include the Graafwater and Peninsula formations of the Table Mountain Group (TMG). Pebbly rocks of the Piekenierskloof Formation occur at the base of the TMG and are well exposed as you climb the Piekenierskloof Pass north of Cape Town along the N7 motor route on the way to Citrusdal. The relatively large, pebble-size rocks that make up the Piekenierskloof conglomerate are not found in the Cape Town area and indicate that TMG sands were sourced from rocks eroded to the north and east of Cape Town.

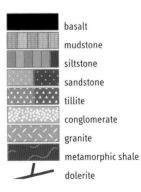

basalt
mudstone
siltstone
sandstone
tillite
conglomerate
granite
metamorphic shale
dolerite

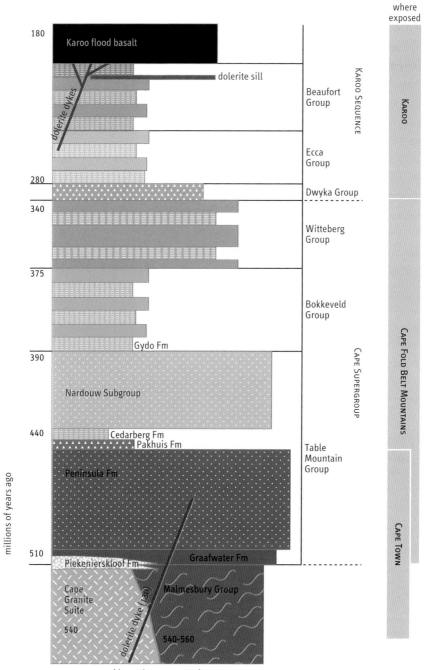

where
exposed

180

Karoo flood basalt

dolerite sill

dolerite dykes

Beaufort
Group

KAROO SEQUENCE

KAROO

Ecca
Group

280

Dwyka Group

340

Witteberg
Group

375

Bokkeveld
Group

Gydo Fm

390

Nardouw Subgroup

CAPE SUPERGROUP

CAPE FOLD BELT MOUNTAINS

440

Cedarberg Fm
Pakhuis Fm

Table
Mountain
Group

Peninsula Fm.

510

Piekenierskloof Fm   Graafwater Fm

Cape
Granite
Suite

540

dolerite dyke (130)

Malmesbury Group

540-560

CAPE TOWN

older rocks not exposed

millions of years ago

As the Graafwater Formation gives way to the Peninsula Formation, you see a complete loss of the distinctive maroon mudstone layers (Fig. 40). The contact between the two formations is usually covered by rock debris and soil, but is clearly visible from a distance as a change in slope, where more resistant overlying Peninsula Formation sandstones rise up vertically to form impressive cliff faces above the Graafwater Formation. These cliffs, so dramatically visible from the city, are stacks upon stacks of amazingly uniform sandstone beds: many are cross-bedded and some have layers rich in quartz pebbles. The Peninsula sandstones on Table Mountain are around 550 m thick but are up to 1 800 m thick elsewhere in the Cape Fold Belt.

The Peninsula Formation rocks are composed almost entirely of quartz sand (98 weight percent) with only minor amounts of iron and manganese oxides and other minerals such as zircon. Quartz is a chemically simple mineral composed of silicon and oxygen (SiO_2). Such well-sorted, quartz-rich sands (Fig. 46) usually form by intense

Figure 42. You can see the alternation of mudstone
and sandstone layers in repeated cycles like
these exposed in the Graafwater Formation along
Tafelberg Road, as well as Chapman's Peak Drive.

SANDSTONE-RICH

MUDSTONE-RICH

weathering and multiple cycles of deposition. These wear down the grains into a spherical shape and leach out all but the most chemically stable minerals, such as quartz. Similar thick sand accumulations formed on other continents and may indicate that fundamentally different sand depositional systems existed before the evolution of large land plants (Fig. 47).

What do these features of the Graafwater and Peninsula formations tell us about the environment in which they were deposited? The contact between the two formations shows no evidence of erosion and geologists do not believe that it represents a significant gap (disconformity) in an otherwise continuous rock record. The transition therefore reflects a sideways shift of two different environments that lay next to each other, most likely in response to a change in sea level (Fig. 47).

A lack of fossils makes interpretation of the Graafwater and Peninsula formation rocks difficult. Some geologists interpret them as ancient river deposits, while other

Figure 43. Rounded bits of mudstone that were ripped up and tumbled as semi-cohesive mud balls are common in the sandstone layers of the Graafwater Formation, as shown here in a slab cut from the contour path near the King's Blockhouse.

Figure 44. The mud units of the Graafwater Formation commonly display ripple marks from the ebb and flow of tidal currents, as well as polygonal sand-filled mud cracks that indicate occasional exposure and desiccation. Here we are looking down on the depositional surface of Graafwater rocks exposed along Chapman's Peak Drive.

Figure 45. Cross-bedded sands of the Graafwater rocks exposed along the contour path (left). Three separate depositional events are interpreted to have formed the rock (the white patches are lichens that only very recently formed on the exposed rock surface). Cross-bedding results from the movement of sediment in the form of ripples or waves. The entire ripple is rarely preserved. More commonly, only the slip face of the ripple is preserved as beds that cross at an angle to the horizontal bedding plane and indicate the direction of current flow.

3 PLANAR BEDS DEPOSITED

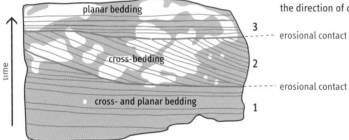

planar bedding

time

3 ------- erosional contact

cross-bedding

2

------- erosional contact

cross- and planar bedding

1

2 CROSS-BEDDED RIPPLES DEPOSITED

current flow direction →

sand particle projectory

deposition

erosion

ripple moves downcurrent →

interior cross-bedding of sand ripple

planar bedding

1 SLIGHTLY CROSS-BEDDED AND PLANAR BEDS DEPOSITED

current flow direction →

cross-bedding

geologists interpret them as beach deposits (Fig. 47). If they are river deposits, then the Graafwater sandstones would have been deposited in fast-flowing river channels while the mudstones settled out of quiet, slack water over the floodplain downriver. The transition to the Peninsula Formation sandstones may represent a change to a large, rapidly flowing braided river system whose muddy floodplain deposits were displaced further downstream in response to a relative drop in sea level.

If they are coastal deposits, then the muddy Graafwater rocks would have been deposited in the quiet estuarine or tidal mud flat behind the beach sands that provided a barrier to large ocean waves. The transition to overlying sands of the Peninsula Formation would represent a rise in sea level that allowed beach sands to cover the muddy lagoon deposits. The rate of sand supply to the coast would then have been matched by a relative rise in sea level for a long period of time, which allowed multiple, stacked beach deposits to build up.

There is support for both of the above scenarios, and it is possible that both were active at different times during deposition.

At the highest elevations of Table Mountain near Maclear's Beacon, you can see exposures of the Pakhuis Formation, whose rocks are unusual because of their jumbled

Figure 46. A slice of Peninsula Formation sandstone, cut thin enough to allow light to pass through it, displays the dark inclusions that define the rounded shapes of individual quartz grains now held together by quartz cement. This rock was originally loose sand similar to beach sand and was only later cemented into a hard rock when it was deeply buried. The high pressure of deep burial caused the grains to dissolve at their points of contact with neighbouring grains. The dissolved quartz then precipitated in the lower-pressure gaps between the grain contacts. In this way, the originally loose sand was transformed into hard sandstone.

Figure 47. (a) (Left) The braided streams and beach deposits along the southern coast of Iceland represent a possible modern (snapshot) analogue to deposition of the Graafwater and Peninsula formations, including the absence of large land plants.

(b) (Right) The two contrasting models for the sideways shift in depositional environments during deposition of the lower TMG: a drop in sea level and advancement of a large river system (bottom), versus a relative rise in sea level and the shift of beach sands over the land (top).

mixture of grains. These range in size from fine mud to coarse gravel and contrast starkly with the well-sorted sandstones of the underlying Peninsula Formation. If you look carefully you may find some weathered-out pebbles with scratched surfaces that indicate that the Pakhuis rocks were deposited at the tail end of a melting glacier. The Pakhuis Formation is also well exposed on the road cut along Michell's Pass just below the Tolhuis and marks a dramatic change to cold, glacial conditions.

Although the Graafwater and Peninsula formations make an impressive pile of sand on the faces of Table Mountain, these sandstones are just the start of the much thicker succession of sandstone and shale that make up the Cape Supergroup (Fig. 41). The entire Cape Supergroup most probably extended throughout the Cape Town area, but the bulk of it has been eroded away, leaving only the lowermost Graafwater and Peninsula rocks of Table Mountain. You can see the rest of the Cape Supergroup rocks by crossing the spectacular passes that cut through the Cape Fold Belt Mountains.

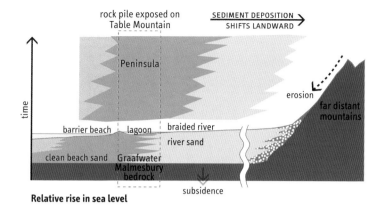

Relative rise in sea level

Relative drop in sea level

In general, you progressively move through the vertical succession of rocks as you travel toward the interior. The sandstone and shale rocks that make up this thick Cape Supergroup are only briefly mentioned here, as they share many of the features already discussed for the Graafwater and Peninsula rocks, such as cross-bedding, ripple marks and cyclic deposition.

On top of the Pakhuis Formation lies the Cedarberg Formation, a widespread but relatively thin shale bed. The soft, easily weathered Cedarberg shale is rarely exposed on the surface, but is often visible from a distance in the Cederberg Mountains as the smooth, sloped areas sandwiched between the more craggy exposures of resistant sandstone, or as valley floors cut by rivers. The Cedarberg shale indicates a low-energy, deep-water marine environment as relative sea level rose in the area. The Cedarberg shale may represent the fine rock 'flour' produced when the massive Pakhuis glaciers pulverised the underlying bedrock. Conditions were at least occasionally suitable for

Figure 48. Brachiopods from the Disa member of the Cedarberg Formation (top). A decapitated marine trilobite (right) and brachiopods (above) from the basal shale (Gydo Formation) of the Bokkeveld Group, which is well exposed along the Gydo Pass road cut outside the town of Ceres. These fossils indicate a relative rise in sea level during deposition of the Cedarberg and Gydo formations.

preserving fossils such as brachiopods (Fig. 48), which indicate an age of around 440 million years. Sea level fell during the coastal deposition of the overlying Nardouw Subgroup cyclic shale and sandstone. The lack of fossils in the Nardouw rocks once again makes it difficult to distinguish between river and coastal environments. The overlying Bokkeveld Group includes a mixture of shale and sandstone, some of which have well-preserved marine fossils (Fig. 48). The Cape Supergroup package is capped once again by the cyclic alternation of shale and sandstone of the Witteberg Group.

In summary, the rocks of Table Mountain and the Cape Fold Belt make up a truly impressive stack of sandstone and shale that constitutes the Cape Supergroup. The Cape Fold Belt Mountains stretch nearly 1 000 km along the south and west margins of South Africa (Fig. 8). Following the uplift and erosion that wore down a flat surface which cut across the Malmesbury shale and granite bedrock, the margin started to sink and went right on sinking at a rate that provided the space for the accumulation of this over 7 km thick pile of sand and mud (Fig. 49). The Cape Supergroup was deposited 510 to 340 million years ago along a passive continental margin as the sea rose and fell, and sediment was delivered by major river systems to the coast from the weathering of highlands to the north. Deep burial cemented the sand into sandstone and compressed the mud into shale.

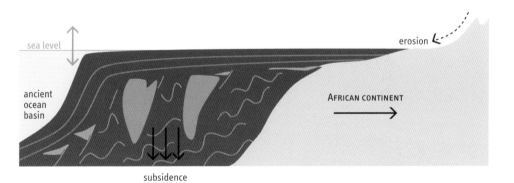

Figure 49. Deposition of the Cape Supergroup on the flat eroded surface of granite-intruded Malmesbury rocks. Alternating deposition of sandstone and shale reflects changes in relative sea level along an overall subsiding, passive continental margin.

The end of Cape Supergroup sedimentation is marked by a large gap in the rock record that persists to the present day over most parts of the Cape Fold Belt. The dramatic folds spectacularly on display along the mountain pass roads that cut through the Cape Fold Belt (Fig. 50) indicate that the sandstones – originally deposited and buried as nearly horizontal layers – experienced major collisional forces, which deformed the Cape Supergroup into a folded, compressed and crumpled-up mass (Fig. 51). The passive, subsiding margin on which the Cape Supergroup sediments had accumulated was transformed into an active, collisional margin; and through a series of episodic pulses of uplift between 280 and 235 million years ago, this gave rise to the Cape Fold Belt Mountains. What we can see today is only the worn-down remnants of what was a much larger mountain chain. This collision was part of a series that resulted in extensive mountain belts and the fusion of continents to form the supercontinent Pangaea (Fig. 52).

Figure 50. Exposure of the large folds of sandstone layers of the Table Mountain Group along Cogman's Kloof outside the town of Montagu.

Partially coinciding with and continuing after the uplift of the Cape Fold Belt, the continent buckled to create the Karoo Basin, a large, bowl-like depression to the north in the interior of the continent. Sediment, much of it eroded from the newly-formed Cape Fold Belt, filled the Karoo Basin with what is referred to as the Karoo Sequence. In this way, the older rock record of the Cape area was largely cannibalised to make the more recent rock record in the Karoo Basin. The transition from the Cape Supergroup to the Karoo Sequence represents a major change in environment. Today the ancient deposits of the Karoo Basin make up the Karoo Plateau, that extensive, relatively flat and dry patch of elevated ground one has to cross to reach Johannesburg.

The Karoo Sequence starts with the Dwyka glacial tillite, a blue-green rock whose hodgepodge of rock bits resembles a dog's breakfast and can be spotted in road cuts as one passes through the Cape Fold Belt toward the interior (Fig. 53). Similar to the Pakhuis Formation on top of Table Mountain, the Dwyka tillite signals a return to cold, glacial conditions as once again the continent drifted close to the South Pole. However,

Figure 51. The Cape Fold Belt formed during a major mountain-building episode as the continents collided to form Pangaea. Volcanic ash deposits in the Karoo Basin indicate the presence of active subduction zones to the west and south as South America and Antarctica came steaming in for a collision with Africa, which crumpled up the more interior Cape Supergroup sandstones into the Cape Fold Belt Mountains.

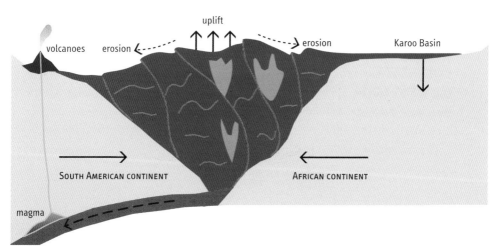

CAPE FOLD BELT

uplift

volcanoes   erosion   erosion   Karoo Basin

SOUTH AMERICAN CONTINENT   AFRICAN CONTINENT

magma

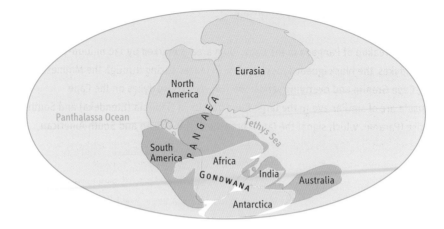

Figure 52. The supercontinent Pangaea at the time when all of the continents came together around 250 million years ago. The enormous Dwyka Ice Sheet covered a large part of Gondwana from 320 to 270 million years ago.

Figure 53. A cut slab of the Dwyka tillite, made up of a wide variety of irregularly shaped rock fragments of varying sizes, all floating in a blue-green muddy matrix that was dumped as the Dwyka Ice Sheet melted.

Dwyka glacial deposits indicate that enormous ice sheets (over 70 million km^2), far more extensive than the present-day ice sheets (15 million km^2), covered the supercontinent from after the deposition of the Cape Supergroup until the start of the Cape Fold Belt deformation, 320 to 270 million years ago. Karoo deposition was terminated by uplift and a profuse outpouring of lava around 180 million years ago. This outpouring of basalt heralded the breakup of Pangaea and forms the Drakensberg mountains in Lesotho, as well as the mesa-like resistant hill tops that you see so conspicuously scattered across the Karoo landscape. Although they were probably not originally deposited in the Cape Town area, the story of the Karoo deposits and the land fossils found there is showcased at the South African Museum in Cape Town.

The initial breakup of Pangaea in the Cape Town area is marked by 130 million-year-old dolerite dykes, the black igneous rock you find in places slicing through the Malmesbury shale, Cape Granite and overlying sandstone (Fig. 54). These dykes on the Cape Peninsula are of similar age to the large flood basalts in Namibia (Etendeka) and South America (Parana), which signal the latest breakup of the African and South American continents. This basaltic magma, fed by rising hot mantle plumes, gradually opened up the South Atlantic Ocean basin, which continues to grow wider to this day.

As more basalt magma arrived at the surface and the Atlantic Ocean grew wider, the edge of the continent cooled and contracted to form a basin in which sediment has accumulated since breakup around 130 million years ago (Fig. 55). The bulk of the sediment in this basin offshore from Cape Town was deposited between 130 and 67 million years ago during the Cretaceous period, as the rifted continent was rapidly weathered under a warm and humid climate. This period of intense weathering created the coastal plain and Great Escarpment. The relatively thin overlying (Tertiary) sediments are mostly made up of small marine fossil shells as the shift to a drier climate greatly reduced the supply of sediment from the continent. Wedges of coarse Cretaceous sediment occur in pockets of the Cape Fold Belt, but most of the Cretaceous and younger

Figure 54. A black dolerite dyke cuts through Cape Granite exposed on the False Bay coast south of Simon's Town at Froggy Pond.

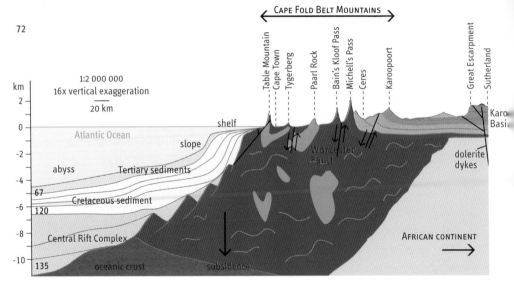

Figure 55. A present-day cross-sectional view of the ruptured edge of the African continent. The age and thickness of sediment in the offshore basin were obtained from the reflection of seismic (wave) energy by the oil industry in search of oil and gas.

deposits have been eroded from the area and recycled back to a retreating sea. The general lack of more recent sediment on land is a result of continued uplift (perhaps related to the southern extension of the East African Rift Valley mantle plume – see Chapter 1) and an overall drop in sea level. Both of these factors have combined to focus sediment deposition in the offshore basin and to erode rather than accumulate deposits in the Cape Town area.

Therefore, the Western Cape has been undergoing erosion or nondeposition since the Dwyka deep freeze and Cape Fold Belt collisional upheaval, when the supercontinent Pangaea was being assembled. As a consequence, our understanding of what happened in the Cape Town area during most of the last 400 million years of geologic time is missing. The Karoo Basin to the north extends the rock record from approximately 280 to 180 million years ago, but then it too stops as Pangaea starts to break apart. However, similar to Cape Town's 130-million-year-old dolerite dykes, the Karoo does have the occasional volcanic eruption – some as recently as 45 million years ago. For example, the diamond-bearing kimberlite pipes, such as the Big Hole at Kimberley, were formed by violent eruptions around 85 million years ago.

So, does that end Cape Town's rock story? Not quite. Bits and pieces of younger deposits exist and these provide valuable clues to the more recent geological history of the Cape Town area.

Cape Town's over 440 million-year-old, exhumed and weathered surface is not without
some youthful rock and sediment. In fact, as is fairly typical of most low-lying coastal
areas throughout the world, the geological map of the Cape Town area shows that large
lowland areas are covered by recent sediment (refer to the geological map, Fig. 80).
But these, like cosmetic makeup, are superficial deposits that cover up older rocks just
below the surface. For example, most of the Cape Flats is covered by sands deposited
within the last several million to several thousand years that form a relatively thin
(less than 50 m thick) veneer over the subsurface Malmesbury shale and Cape Granite
bedrock. These more recent deposits, although limited in extent and thin, are important
because we interact with them most directly; together with the more complete sediment

Figure 56. An excavated fossil bed on display to
visitors at the West Coast Fossil Park, divided into
one square metre areas (left). A close-up of the
jaw bone and teeth of a short-necked giraffe,
40 cm long (bottom left). Many of the larger bones
are from the short-necked giraffes (sivatheres),
but fossil bear, pig, seal and sabre-toothed cats
as well as an abundance of frog bones are among
the remains of animals that coexisted along what
was probably a river course or wetland near the
sea 5 million years ago.

Figure 57. A drawing of the now extinct short-
necked giraffes (sivatheres) once found in the
region of the West Coast Fossil Park.

records we find offshore, they provide us with clues to more recent changes in the Cape Town area.

The oldest of these relatively young deposits occurs about an hour and a half's drive north of Cape Town at the old phosphate quarry recently transformed into the West Coast Fossil Park, located off the R27 opposite the town of Langebaan (Fig. 80). Phosphate rock was mined until 1995 for the production of phosphoric acid, which is widely used as fertiliser and is the principal acid in cooldrinks such as Coca-Cola. The phosphate rock formed at a time when the sea level was relatively high and phosphorus, a minor but important component of living organisms, was released as bacteria broke down dead organic remains buried in the sediment. So much phosphorus was released that it combined with calcium to form the mineral apatite. The phosphate deposit is at least 5 million years old, as indicated by several fossil-rich beds uncovered during mining of the deposit (Fig. 56). These fossils provide a rare window into the animals living in the area at the time (Fig. 57). Most of these animals are now extinct and many are not known to have lived in any other part of Africa.

Abundant phosphate deposits which are up to 25 million years old also occur offshore. These phosphate rocks mark the transition from the relatively warm and humid climate of the Cretaceous to the cool and dry climate of today. Tectonic reorganisation of the continents after Pangaea broke apart led to changes in ocean circulation that resulted in a major change in global climate. Thick ice sheets covered Antarctica and led to cooler and windier conditions. Strong winds caused upwelling of ocean waters offshore that supplied nutrients to support the growth of abundant marine life in the Benguela upwelling system, which continues to the present day.

The increase in aridity and wind is reflected in the abundance of wind-blown sand deposits along the West Coast (Fig. 58). Strong southerly winds, referred to locally as the Cape Doctor or Southeaster, can blow at gale force (greater than 55 km per hour) for up to 20 percent of the summer season. These winds are well known for blowing air pollu-

Figure 58. A map of the large, modern sand dune deposits on the West Coast. North of Cape Town the amount of rainfall drops off and so does the number of perennial rivers that feed sand to the beach. As a result the amount of windblown sand also tends to decrease from south to north, with the largest active dune fields (prior to the planting of alien vegetation) being on the Cape Flats and smaller dune fields at Atlantis and Yzerfontein–Geelbek further up the coast. The offshore islands provide a barrier to the swell and allow fine sand to accumulate on the protected mainland beaches, where the wind picks it up and moves it inland as sand cordons. The inset shows active dunes 20 m high at Geelbek riding over a 70 000-year-old white calcrete layer.

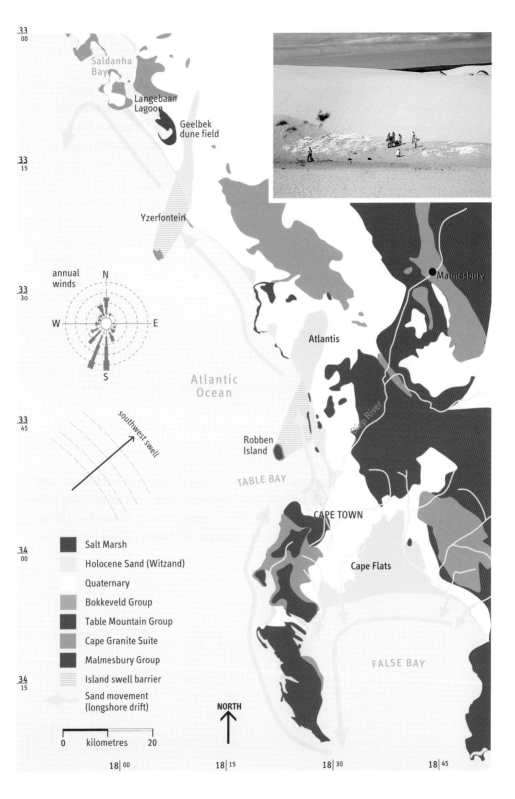

33 00

Saldanha
Bay

Langebaan
Lagoon

Geelbek
dune field

33 15

Yzerfontein

annual
winds

N

W — E

S

33 30

Atlantic
Ocean

Atlantis

Malmesbury

33 45

southwest swell

Diep River

Robben
Island

TABLE BAY

CAPE TOWN

34 00

Cape Flats

Salt Marsh

Holocene Sand (Witzand)

Quaternary

Bokkeveld Group

Table Mountain Group

Cape Granite Suite

Malmesbury Group

Island swell barrier

Sand movement
(longshore drift)

34 15

FALSE BAY

NORTH

0   kilometres   20

18 00   18 15   18 30   18 45

tion away, keeping temperatures cool and producing the cloud drape or 'tablecloth' that supplies moisture to Table Mountain. These winds also pick up fine sand exposed on the dried-out upper reaches of Cape beaches and carry it inland to form sand dunes.

As the waves of the predominant southwest swell break on Cape Town's beaches, the sand travels up the beach face in a skewed trajectory. The net effect is to send the sand northward in what is called longshore or littoral drift. This moving body of sand along the coast is in turn fed by rivers, as well as by coastal erosion and the breakdown of shells in the surf zone. The wind taps off approximately one-third of the beach sand migrating up the coast to form dunes, which return sand back onto the land.

The extent and size of coastal dunes are highly variable along the beaches of the Western Cape. Large coastal dunes tend to form along relatively coarse sandy beaches, or where rapidly growing vegetation traps the sand. Smaller, mobile sand dunes tend to migrate inland away from fine sandy beaches or into more arid and less vegetated areas. These inland migrating dunes can become stable and immobile if they are vegetated, and can be destabilised back to mobile sand if fire exposes the sand to wind.

Figure 59. A bird's-eye view of Hout Bay beach taken in 1944, which shows the white dune cordon stretching from the beach over the saddle on its way to Sandy Bay on the other side.

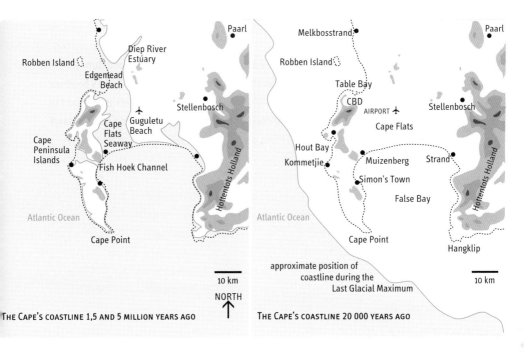

Figure 60. The Cape Peninsula shoreline in the case of (a) a 25 m higher stand of sea level that occurred around 5 and 1,5 million years ago when it was an island, and (b) a 125 m lower stand of sea level at the time of maximum ice buildup during cold periods – the most recent being 20 000 years ago.

In some cases, the sand blown across land eventually returns to the coast. A good example of such a local headland bypass dune is in Hout Bay where, until beach dunes were artificially planted, sand was blown from Hout Bay Beach over the saddle to Sandy Bay (Fig. 59).

Ancient dune deposits under the Namib Sand Sea indicate that these strong southerly winds have blown for the last 20-odd million years, but the oldest known dune deposit in the Cape Town area is around 5 million years old. These dunes occur north of the town of Saldanha and are currently mined for their high (90 percent) shell content. They may have originated at the same time as the land fossils of the West Coast Fossil Park, 20 km to the southeast. The beach and dune deposits near Saldanha indicate that the sea was 25 m higher than today both 5 and 1,5 million years ago. A sea level 25 m higher than today would have made the Cape Peninsula a large island separated from the African mainland by a narrow seaway over the Cape Flats (Fig. 60).

ICE AND SEA LEVEL

Currently Earth, in contrast to most of its history, has a large amount of water tied up as ice on Antarctica – enough, in fact, to raise sea level by 65 m if it were to melt. Over the last million years the amount of ice has varied considerably as Earth's climate has cycled approximately every 100 000 years between relatively warm and cold periods. The maximum buildup of ice during the most recent cold period 20 000 years ago dropped the sea level 125 m – a testimony to the enormous amount of water trapped in Northern Hemisphere ice sheets if you consider that over 70 percent of Earth's surface is covered by ocean. Sea level then rose (as rapidly as 30 cm in ten years) to near its present-day position, as the large Northern Hemisphere (NH) ice sheets (except Greenland) melted between 20 000 and 7 000 years ago.

Figure 61. Wave-cut marine terraces at Kommetjie (left). The notch at the base of Slangkop Hill was cut both at 5 and 1,5 million years ago during a 25 m higher sea level. The present-day intertidal terrace which extends out to sea was cut during warmer interglacial periods such as today (Fig. 62). Noordhoek Beach is in the foreground.

Figure 62. Estimated variations in sea level in response to the amount of water stored as ice over the last 140 000 years (below). The shelly beach sands of the Velddrif Formation were deposited during the last warm (interglacial) period and the overlying dune sands of the Langebaan Formation were deposited as the sea started to drop between 120 000 and 80 000 years ago.

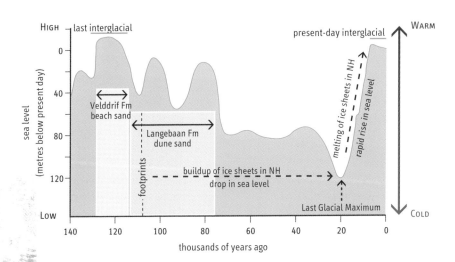

You can see evidence of higher past sea levels along the coast where waves have eroded the rock surface flat to form marine terraces (Fig. 61). Terraces also occur offshore, cut by waves during times when the sea was lower. Gravels on these terraces are mined for diamonds along the coast north of Cape Town. During the last million or so years, the height of the sea has repeatedly fallen by 125 m and risen to as much as 10 m above its present level in response to the buildup and then melting of enormous ice sheets in the Northern Hemisphere (Fig. 62). At the height of cold periods (glacials), when the sea level was 125 m lower than today, Robben Island was no longer an island as the Cape Peninsula shoreline retreated between 5 and 30 km seaward (Fig. 60). The sand cover on the coastal plains surrounding Cape Town is composed of a complex mosaic of different-aged beach and dune deposits, reflecting the way in which the position of the beach shifted repeatedly in the past in response to changes in sea level.

Figure 63. An eroded cliff exposure of beach and dune sand deposits at Kraalbaai along the western margin of Langebaan Lagoon in the West Coast National Park. The dark-coloured rocks near the shore are Velddrif beach sands and the steeply cross-bedded white dune sand deposits are part of the Langebaan Formation and include the Preekstoel (pulpit). The hills in the background are made up of Cape Granite with wave-cut terraces visible in the distant far right.

One of the best exposures of past beach and dune deposits can be seen along the western cliffs of Langebaan Lagoon in the West Coast National Park (Fig. 63). The park is about an hour and a half's drive north of the city, with a southern entrance off the R27 and a northern entrance through the town of Langebaan. The park is centred on Langebaan Lagoon, a north-south tidal lagoon 20 km long with extensive salt marshes, intertidal sand flats and subtidal channels. At the base of the cliffs, very near the present-day high-tide waterline, the shelly beach sands of the Velddrif Formation are well exposed. The shells in the Velddrif are different from those that you find along the West Coast today and indicate warmer water conditions and a slightly higher sea level during the previous warm period from 135 000 to 125 000 years ago. As the global climate became colder, ice buildup lowered sea level. The shelly beach sands of the Velddrif Formation were covered by large coastal dunes of the Langebaan Formation during this period of variable but generally lower sea level from approximately 125 000 to 75 000 years ago (Fig. 62). The coastal dunes were abandoned as the sea retreated

Figure 64. A white calcrete layer at the top of the Kraalbaai cliffs with brown sand and plants above. Calcrete is a hard, carbonate-cemented rock that commonly forms in Mediterranean climates and is widespread in the subsurface of the Western Cape. The brown sand above has had its calcite shell fragments leached out of it by acidic soil waters, which then percolate downward to precipitate out the calcite to form the calcrete layer.

more rapidly from the continued growth of ice sheets in the Northern Hemisphere. Stabilised by vegetation, these dune sands became partially cemented and formed sub-surface calcrete layers (Fig. 64).

In addition to old dune deposits along Langebaan Lagoon, you can see modern moving dunes in the West Coast National Park, both near the Geelbek visitors' centre and along the Atlantic beaches (Fig. 58). The modern dunes are clearly distinguishable from the older dunes because they are covered by less vegetation and are whiter in colour, since less time has been available to dissolve their white carbonate shell fragments. At the southern end of the park, the Geelbek dune cordon comes off the beach north of the town of Yzerfontein and extends 24 km inland. These high dunes (up to 20 m) made up of fine sand have been clocked moving at 10 m per year – an impressive and believable rate of advance once you have been sandblasted while standing among them on a typical summer afternoon.

Figure 65. A summary timeline of the ups and downs of Cape Town's 560 million year geological history.

We have seen that the rocks preserved in the Cape Town area provide us with glimpses into its complex 560 million year history (Fig. 65). The area alternated between periods of subsidence under extensional, pulling tectonic forces and periods of uplift under compressional, collisional tectonic forces. These reversals in tectonic force most likely relate to reorganisation of heat transfer via hot plumes rising from the deep mantle to the surface. At times these rising mantle plumes sent the African and other continents colliding together and at times they split Africa and the other continents apart. As the African continent was pushed around the globe, it sometimes sat at the warm and humid low latitudes, while other times it sat near the South Pole bearing a thick mantle of ice.

When the African continent was split apart, subsidence of the trailing edge of the continent provided a basin for sediment to accumulate in; where the sediment has been preserved it provides us with a record of how environments evolved along the margin. When Africa collided with other continents, the margin of the continent was pushed up and the accumulated deeper and older rocks on the edge of the continent were compressed, uplifted and eroded to produce gaps in the rock record. In the Cape Town area, the alternating breakups and collisions have generally happened again and again along the same continental suture or linear rupture zone.

Because the Cape Town area has experienced uplift since the collision that formed the supercontinent Pangaea, most of the rocks are old, eroded remnants. Some young deposits have managed to survive on land as well as offshore on the edge of the continent, and these provide important clues to how the region has changed since the most recent breakup of Africa from South America over 135 million years ago. It is on these old rock remnants as well as young surface deposits that we humans have focused our activities in our quest for food, water and building materials.

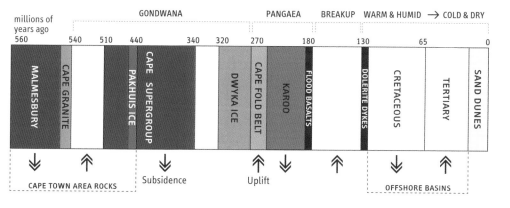

CHAPTER 3

Living on the rocks

Figure 66. The view from Mowbray Ridge looking across the Cape Flats to Table Bay and the hills of Tygerberg.

In Cape Town's hundreds of millions of years of geological history presented in Chapter 2, humans don't feature. Our earliest human ancestors appear only on New Year's Eve in our calendar year of Earth history (around 5 to 7 million years ago), and humans similar to us have been around only in the last 20 minutes (200 000 years). And yet modern humans, particularly over the last 10 000 years (the last minute of Earth history as one calendar year), have had an alarming and accelerating impact on Earth's surface environments. Our success at using natural resources to survive and multiply has resulted in alterations of the local as well as the global environment (Figs. 66 & 67). It is as if, having arrived late to the party, we are hell-bent on making up for lost time. Humans have so altered the landscape and atmosphere, particularly since the Industrial Revolution, that our activities are now considered a geological force in their own right and a new geological period has been proposed: the Anthropocene (the human period).

Human activities have a large and visible impact on Cape Town's landscape. Buildings, roads and agricultural fields dominate the lowland areas; the air is filled with the background hum of activity; and, on still winter days, a brown blanket of smog hangs over the city and Cape Flats (Fig. 68). Cape Town is blessed by the close proximity of rugged mountains that provide a natural green space to these developed lowlands, but even the surrounding mountain areas have not entirely escaped human influence, with their large reservoirs, pine plantations and hiking trails. In this chapter we explore the impacts of human activities on the environments and landscapes of Cape Town.

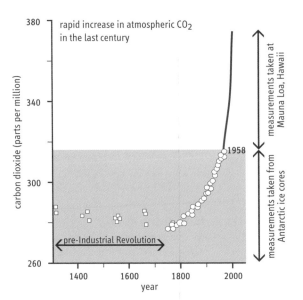

Figure 67. The record of increasing carbon dioxide gas in the atmosphere.

Figure 68. A layer of brown haze (smog) hangs over the Cape Flats, partially obscuring the mountains to the east, as viewed on a winter's morning from the University of Cape Town campus.

GREENHOUSE GASES

Perhaps one of the most alarming human impacts is the rapid increase in the amount of carbon dioxide (CO_2) and methane gas in the atmosphere, in part because, although it is undetected by our senses, we are immersed in it globally (Fig. 67). Carbon dioxide and methane gases are present in relatively minor quantities but they play an important role in retaining heat in Earth's atmosphere. Along with water vapour, these gases capture some of the energy that Earth continuously radiates out to cold space. By capturing and transferring this energy to the atmosphere, these gases maintain a temperature significantly higher than would be the case if they were not present. They are referred to as greenhouse gases by analogy to the window panes of a greenhouse.

The increase in greenhouse gases can be attributed to the burning of fossil fuels (coal, oil, natural gas) and land use changes (destruction of forest; increase in rice paddies, cattle, concrete, etc.). The increase in these gases is accompanied by an increase in their removal by Earth processes in the oceans and on land. These reactions provide 'negative feedbacks' to the increase in CO_2 and will eventually take out much of the CO_2 we are currently adding to the atmosphere. The problem is that the rate of removal is slow compared to the rate at which we are adding CO_2. It will take tens of thousands to hundreds of thousands of years before the excess CO_2 currently being pumped into the atmosphere is removed. Not much comfort to worries of significant global climate change in the coming century.

If you look carefully while walking along coastal areas of the Western Cape, you are likely to find evidence of earlier human occupation. Old rubbish heaps, or middens, are the most common evidence of human activities and contain mostly discarded mussel and limpet shells piled into mounds or scattered over the surface (Fig. 69). These shell-fish were collected from their rocky coastal habitats and carried up to several kilometres away to be consumed by people episodically living in the area. Most of these middens, like the rock paintings in the Cederberg Mountains, are less than 2 000 years old.

Stone tools found scattered on weathered, wind-deflated surfaces indicate that our human ancestors have been in the Western Cape region for at least the last 500 000 and perhaps the last million years. There is as yet no bone or stone tool evidence of our earlier human ancestors, like the 3- to 5-million-year-old fossils from Taung in the

Figure 69. A typical accumulation of discarded shellfish (midden) in coastal dunes next to Langebaan Lagoon at Kraalbaai. The midden is located above the calcrete layer of Figure 64. Radiocarbon analysis (Fig. 34) of limpet shells from the bottom of this layer reveals that it has been a popular picnic site for the last 1 600 years.

Figure 70. The opening to Peers Cave in the TMG sandstones above the town of Fish Hoek. The cave contains evidence of Cape Town's early human habitants, such as rock paintings (right) and tools made from sandstone and silcrete, a finely crystalline quartz rock (below).

Northern Cape and from the Sterkfontein caves at the Cradle of Humankind World Heritage Site near Johannesburg.

Stone tools and other artefacts from Peers Cave, located in the Table Mountain Group sandstones above the Fish Hoek Valley (Fig. 70), indicate that Cape Town's early human inhabitants used the shelter on and off for the last 200 000 years. Unfortunately, the record of human occupation at Peers Cave was largely destroyed by the crude methods used during its initial excavation – methods that included the use of dynamite! More recently, human footprints approximately 100 000 years old were found remarkably preserved in old dune sand deposits at Langebaan Lagoon (Fig. 63). Similarly aged stone artefacts were recovered from open-air sites exposed in the Geelbek dunefield adjacent to Langebaan Lagoon (Fig. 58), excavated from cave sites along the West Coast at Yzerfontein, and found along the South Coast at Blombos Cave. These late Middle Stone Age sites, spanning from roughly 100 000 to 20 000 years ago, are of particular interest because it was during this time that the first evidence has been found to suggest abstract thought expressed as symbols or art.

These early human inhabitants of the Cape Peninsula were probably largely similar to the San (Bushmen), living by hunting and gathering and roaming the countryside in search of fresh water and game. They made use of marine resources such as intertidal shellfish, made stone tools from locally derived rocks and used emptied ostrich eggs to carry water. Their impact was probably small because of their small numbers, and the extent to which they manipulated the environment was probably limited to the use of fire.

Pastoralists – people who herd sheep and cattle – migrated from the northeast into the Western Cape around 2 000 to 1 600 years ago. The pastoralists interacted with the hunter-gathers through trade in pottery and ostrich eggshell beads. The human population as well as the number of grazing herds increased during this time. The environmental impact of these early inhabitants included the partial conversion of renosterveld to grassland, perhaps by use of fire, and the displacement of wild by domesticated herds. These changes were relatively small compared to those that would occur later upon arrival and expansion of industrial populations from Europe. Many of these changes have been touched upon already. Here we examine in greater depth how in the pursuit of controlling our environment and obtaining natural resources, we have significantly and often adversely altered environments in the Cape Town area.

A far more visible impact of human activities than the increase in greenhouse gases is alteration of the landscape. The burning of natural vegetation to grow crops, and the building of fences, dams, roads and cities, all result in the destruction of what were the habitats of plants and animals prior to the arrival of humans. The fragmentation and destruction of natural habitats has resulted in the rapid loss of species both locally and globally. It is estimated that the rate of species loss is greater now than during Earth's past mass extinction events, in which more than half of the species on Earth were lost as a result of environmental changes brought about by large-scale volcanic activity and extraterrestrial (asteroid) impacts.

In addition to habitat destruction, the introduction of alien vegetation by European settlers has had a major impact on Cape Town's environments. The low-lying Cape Flats have suffered the greatest impact from the displacement of vegetation by farming, buildings and roads. Human activity has been so widespread and so effective in altering the low-lying areas that incomplete relics of the original Cape Flats lowland fynbos survive in only a few small areas, such as the inside oval of the century-old Kenilworth Racecourse and Rondebosch Common.

Alien plants were considered desirable and necessary at the time to make the area hospitable and profitable. Much of the indigenous renosterveld vegetation on the low-lying and fertile soils of the Malmesbury rocks has been replaced by wheat as well as vineyards to support a large agricultural industry. Most of the once-mobile dune sands on the Cape Flats are now stable because of the planting of Australian acacias such as Port Jackson. The residents of the Cape Flats are spared the nuisance of wind-blown sand and the large alien bushes provide shade and wind breaks as well as wood for fire and building not obtainable from the smaller indigenous plants. Many of the mountain slopes are covered by pine forests, which once provided an important source of wood for fuel and building. Hiking through the pines of Cecilia Plantation (which are now being felled in order to reinstate the indigenous vegetation) has always been a distinct experience from walking on the more exposed, windy and sunny trails on the fynbos slopes of Table Mountain; the smell of pine sap is reminiscent of home to Northern Hemisphere visitors. And some might argue that the tall, flat-topped stone pines indigenous to the Mediterranean give the hills around Rhodes Memorial and the Cableway end of Tafelberg Road a more interesting, majestic look. Why then the concern over alien plants if they have proved so useful and have added new dimensions to the landscape?

Today we have a very different perspective from that of the early European settlers because of a greater understanding of ecosystems and because we are now witness

to some of the negative as well as positive consequences of introducing alien species to the Cape. Many of the aliens planted for the purpose of stabilising the dune sand (primarily the Australian acacias Port Jackson, rooikrans and black wattle) have spread rapidly into other environments where, rather than providing economic or practical benefits, they are having large detrimental impacts on the ecosystem. It is the unpredicted and rapid spread of these alien plants that is of greatest concern. From both a practical and an ecological point of view, the largest negative impacts of alien plants have been an accelerating loss of water, topsoil and biodiversity.

Loss of biodiversity refers to a reduction in the total number of species of plants and animals. The Cape Floral Region is remarkable for its large number of different plant species that live in a relatively small area. For example, it contains over 500 species of heather (ericas), even though the differences between these species may be subtle. Furthermore, many fynbos species are restricted to specific mountain environments on the Cape Peninsula. But, you might wonder, wouldn't the introduction of new and additional species to an ecosystem increase biodiversity? Initially, yes, but where alien species so effectively out-compete indigenous plants, the diverse indigenous plants of an area are rapidly replaced by one or two successful alien species over time. The ability to proliferate varies hugely among alien plants. Eucalyptus trees grow relatively slowly and are not particularly invasive, whereas the Australian acacias are extremely aggressive.

The loss of species is alarming and readily apparent. If you walk through a grove of eucalyptus, rooikrans or pine, you will notice the almost complete absence of other plants as they are either shaded or crowded out. An area once characterised by several hundred different species now contains only one species. Remember too that not all of those hundreds of replaced fynbos species are widespread. Some will have grown only in that particular area where the alien species has taken over, so that the alien newcomer has effectively caused the extinction of the indigenous species. And once extinct, a species can never be recovered. The side effects of invasion are also visually striking: the soil is often bare or rocky with large alien roots unable to retain the thin fine topsoil,

Figure 71. The stark contrast between a highly diverse fynbos ecosystem (ericas in foreground; large protea bush to the right) and a grove of cork oaks on the slopes of Table Mountain. The heavily shaded interior of the cork oak grove reveals the severe loss of smaller plants and topsoil from underneath the cork oaks (inset).

the number of insects is greatly diminished and the area is less aesthetically pleasing, with far fewer textures and colours (Fig. 71).

If fynbos plants have spent millions of years adapting to the specific environments of the Cape region, why is it that they are being out-competed by alien invaders? The success of the aliens is based on their ability to make a living out of nutrient-poor soils. Indeed, many Australian soils are more impoverished than those of the Cape region. In addition, alien plants have deep-penetrating roots to tap underground sources of water and are no longer hampered by pests and diseases of their homeland. But perhaps most importantly, they, like the fynbos, are adapted to fire, but have the great advantage of producing viable seeds after only one year of growth. Many fynbos plants require on average seven years before their seeds are mature. Alien plants are also larger than fynbos plants and hence fuel hotter, more intense fires that make them a far greater fire hazard to surrounding communities. If fire reoccurs every two rather than ten years, then the Australian acacia seeds, but not the fynbos seeds, are mature and able to sprout. Therefore, the spread of alien plants has benefited from human activities which have greatly increased the frequency of fires on the Cape Peninsula.

In addition to the loss of biodiversity, alien plants greatly increase water loss from the environment. The deep tap roots and large size of alien plants allow them to act like big water pumps: extracting water from below the surface and transpiring it out to the atmosphere through their leaves, where it is blown away by the dry summer wind. This extraction of groundwater by alien plants to the atmosphere, water that was otherwise destined to flow in streams or springs, draws down water levels and endangers the health of the ecosystem. Hence, the primary argument to eradicate alien vegetation is to save precious water. The Department of Water Affairs and Forestry has instituted the Working for Water Programme to increase employment and to remove the deleterious alien plants – a very worthwhile but extremely difficult task given the pervasiveness and resilience of the alien invaders.

Therefore, the widespread invasion of alien plants diminishes the ecosystem by significantly reducing its water, species diversity and beauty. Degradation of the ecosystem renders it less useful in the long run to humans as well. Soils are no longer as fertile, there is less water available, landscapes are less attractive to tourists, and potential medicinal and other uses of extinct indigenous plants are lost forever. But we need to grow food, and relatively fast-growing shade trees are pleasant to have around in summer. The solution may be in a compromise to limit the number and extent of alien species. To try to completely remove these plants and return the environment to its original condition would be impractical, but stopping the unintentional rapid spread of alien plants that have such a large negative impact must be a priority to prevent further degradation of the ecosystem.

The need for fresh water is one of the major factors that influenced early and later inhabitants of the Cape. Many ancient sites of human occupation are situated near water courses or seasonal springs, and the early Dutch settlers abandoned Saldanha Bay as an ideal harbour for lack of fresh water. After people settled in Cape Town, their activities were soon limited by the scarcity of sources of fresh water and it became necessary to build dams, first upon Table Mountain and later in the Hottentots Holland Mountains. But as soon as new water resources were established, use would outstrip supply and thus began a never-ending escalation in the quest for fresh water. The emphasis has now shifted to water conservation and to promoting an awareness of just how precious water is because of the economic and ecological costs of supplying it. South Africans are not alone in their concerns about water. The World Health Organisation estimates that nearly one in six people on Earth lacks access to sufficient fresh water.

We are all familiar with how water arrives in Cape Town as rainfall that then soaks into the soil or runs off the surface into streams to return eventually to the ocean. But the pathway of water is more complicated than this because of its long-term interaction with the vegetation, soil and underlying sediments and rocks (Fig. 72).

The rain that falls in Cape Town is nearly pure, with only 20 grams of dissolved salts (mostly sodium chloride or table salt) in every 1 000 litres of water. The salt content of water running off Table Mountain remains low because the rocks are mainly made up of quartz, which is only slightly soluble in water. The water that flows off Table Mountain is acidic (with measured pH values of less than 4) because it picks up CO_2 from the organic-rich fynbos soils through which it seeps and because Table Mountain rocks lack feldspar or carbonate minerals that can react with and neutralise the acidic waters (Fig. 21). These waters also leach soluble organic compounds from the fynbos soil to give mountain streams a distinct yellow to brown colour similar to that of rooibos tea.

The water that resides in the pores and fractures of subsurface sediment and rock is referred to as groundwater. An aquifer is a system of specific subsurface sediment or rock layers that contains substantial and extractable quantities of groundwater. For example, many homes have shallow boreholes that tap the water-saturated sands of the Cape Flats aquifer to water their gardens. The quality of water from the Cape Flats aquifer varies, often smelling of rotten eggs (as a result of hydrogen sulphide gas generated by microorganisms), and it can stain surfaces orange when the iron in the water is oxidised upon exposure to air. Near-surface aquifers are also more prone to contamination from leaking petrol and septic tanks, and over-extraction of water from areas near the coast can destroy the aquifer by intrusion of sea water. In built-up areas such as Cape

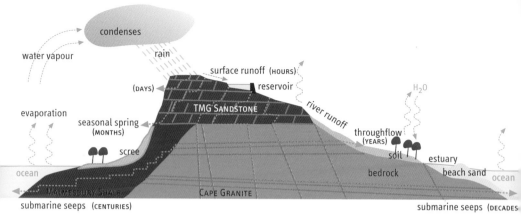

Figure 72. A simplified schematic diagram of Cape Town's hydrologic cycle, showing the pathways that water can follow in its cycling between land and sea.

Town, rainwater is quickly lost as runoff from rooftops, tarred and concrete surfaces. Rapid runoff results in more flooding and less seepage of water into soils to replenish groundwater in urban areas.

Groundwater can also occur in rocks to great depths below the surface and in places makes up an important natural long-term reservoir of water. The Table Mountain Group sandstones of the Cape Fold Belt collectively contain vast quantities of groundwater and are actively being explored as an additional source of fresh water to help meet Cape Town's ever-increasing demand. For example, groundwater extraction is currently being tested at several trial boreholes in the Olifants River Valley near Citrusdal (Fig. 73).

Figure 73. A section cut through the deep Table Mountain Group aquifer in the large fold (syncline) of the Olifants River Valley. Cool rainwater enters the elevated rocky exposures of the Cederberg Mountains on the eastern side of the valley and makes its way slowly down through the fractured rock to exit eventually on the western side of the valley. Because the column of water in the eastern flank of rock is higher, the water naturally flows through the rocks to exit in the Olifants River Valley. At the Baths resort near Citrusdal water flows out at natural warm springs at a temperature of 43°C. The water is warmed during its slow, deep journey through the folded rocks.

- Bokkeveld Group
- Nardouw Subgroup
- Cedarberg Shale
- Peninsula Fm
- Graafwater Fm
- Piekenierskloof Fm
- Malmesbury Group
- Groundwater flow

Fresh water is obtained by evaporation, mostly as nearly pure water from the salty sea but also from plants and from water on land, such as rivers, reservoirs and lawn sprinklers. Water in the air then condenses to form clouds and rain. Much of the rain that falls on land is evaporated back into the atmosphere, runs off the surfaces and flows into rivers. Alternatively, it soaks into the soil and percolates down into the underlying rocks to be taken up by plants or to continue flowing into the fractured bedrock at depths below the reach of plant roots (Fig. 72). Groundwater flows slowly through sediment or bedrock to emerge later along river courses. Because of the low flow rates, owing to the small size of the connected cracks and pores of the sediment or rock, the time interval between rainwater seeping into the ground and emerging back on the surface as river water can be hundreds to thousands of years. For this reason, rivers with large enough catchments can flow the entire year, even in areas like Cape Town where rainfall is seasonal.

The idea of using groundwater is similar to the principle behind a surface dam: to extract groundwater during dry periods of the year or during drought periods and to allow replenishment of groundwater during the rainy season. But the building of dams, canalisation of rivers and extraction of groundwater all contribute to altering the natural flow of water and the sediment it carries through the environment. Groundwater extraction may lower the subsurface water level (water table) and reduce the flow of water in springs and rivers. The reduced flow could then endanger surface ecosystems that depend on water for their sustainability, particularly during dry periods when these ecosystems are already stressed.

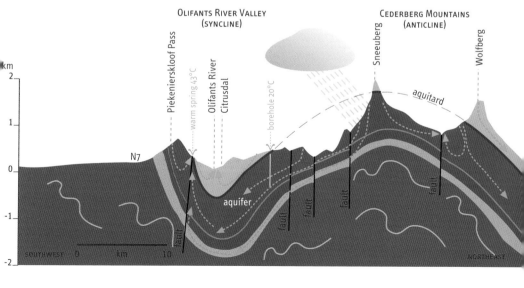

Much of the Cape Town landscape has been rearranged and sculpted to accommodate roads, control water flow and make new land for building. The dramatic proximity of Table Mountain to the city centre has limited the amount of land for building, and for this reason a major earth-moving project was initiated around the Second World War to expand the harbour and the amount of land available for new buildings by filling in the southern end of Table Bay. The original shoreline of the bay ran along what is today Strand Street, and land to the north, which includes the railway station and Foreshore, was established by filling in of the bay. In addition to harbour dredging, much of the fill came from Rietvlei, the large lake between Milnerton and Table View.

Quarries are another example of human-altered landscape. Relatively small quarries around Cape Town are located near Kloofnek, where granite was quarried for the building of Rhodes Memorial, and above De Waal Drive, where Malmesbury rock was extracted for bricks. The much larger current Malmesbury brick mine is visible from the N7 as a large excavated chunk of the Tygerberg hills. Malmesbury shale was also obtained from the old Van Riebeeck Quarry on Robben Island and used as a building stone. Granite quarried for the extra-hard concrete specified for the Koeberg nuclear power plant is clearly visible as the large rectangular cut from the side of the rounded granite hills on the right-hand side of the R27 heading toward the West Coast National Park.

A less obvious alteration of the landscape, but a more widespread and traumatic one to the environment, is the loss of topsoil. Topsoil is the dark, organic-rich, loamy sediment essential for plant growth whose generally loose and fine-sized particles are easily removed by wind and running water, particularly from thin fynbos soils. Exposure of bare soil by ploughing of agricultural fields, trampling of vegetation by animals including humans and the growth of alien vegetation such as pine or eucalyptus can result in significant loss of topsoil (Fig. 74). The making of soil is a long and drawn-out process that requires centuries to millennia. Once topsoil is lost, the land is permanently degraded. This is a major concern in agricultural areas of the Western Cape. Soil loss is further exacerbated by retention of river sediment behind dam walls upstream and the control of river courses that does not allow replenishment of fine sediment to river floodplains. Most of the river courses in the Cape Town area have been canalised and many of their adjacent natural wetlands destroyed. The destruction of these wetland environments has greatly reduced the biodiversity of the area and the natural ability of the sediment and plants of the wetlands to filter out toxic metals carried by the river.

Figure 74. Ploughed fields, poorly designed hiking trails (shown here below the King's Blockhouse) and groves of alien vegetation result in the long-term loss of valuable topsoil.

The Western Cape is fortunate because it isn't subject to much in the way of natural disasters. Ocean waters are too cold to support hurricanes or typhoons and tornadoes are rare. Occasional large winter storms erode and destroy coastal homes and freak waves occasionally claim a fisherman along the South Coast, but tsunamis or tidal waves are not recorded. Volcanic eruptions are nonexistent and earthquakes are not common. But Cape Town is not without its geohazards. Earth seems so large and stable, but it does move and rocks slip and fall. The Tulbagh–Ceres earthquake on 29 September 1969 measured 6,3 on the Richter scale, claimed nine lives and damaged many structures (Fig. 75). Before we had seismographs to measure earthquake magnitude, there are written records of several earthquakes in Cape Town in the early 1800s. Based on the eyewitness descriptions of what was felt and seen, these earthquakes are considered comparable in magnitude to the Tulbagh–Ceres quake. Capetonians are by and large unaware of the potential for earthquakes. Most homes are built of rigid, non-

Figure 75. The Tulbagh–Ceres earthquake of 1969 extensively damaged buildings, including the Drostdy in Tulbagh, now restored.

Figure 76. A major rock fall from the cliffs of Table Mountain to the west of the King's Blockhouse, with the large block of missing rock above and the large sandstone boulders below.

reinforced masonry walls and no mention of earthquakes is made in standard insurance policies. The likelihood or probability of a large earthquake is small but real, and therefore the specific hazards of an earthquake need to be included in Cape Town's detailed generic emergency preparedness plan.

A more familiar geohazard is falling rock, especially along Chapman's Peak Drive, which was closed recently after several motorists had been struck by blocks of falling TMG sandstone. The drive has been redesigned to lessen the chances of rocks falling on road traffic by building overhead structures that capture falling rocks and protect the road at high-risk points. Older large rock falls are visible along many of the margins of Table Mountain (Fig. 76). In addition to rock falls, entire slopes can move as large mud- or debris-flows (Fig. 77). The greatest potential for mudslides is when early heavy winter rains follow a large summer fire that has removed vegetation from mountain slopes. The soil becomes saturated with water and, without the plants to hold it in place, it can creep or flow down the slope as a large mass of muddy sediment. Some of these large, old rock falls and mudflows may have been triggered by earthquakes.

Another expression of rocks on the move is the trillions of sand grains that make

Figure 77. (Left) A road cut below the King's Blockhouse on Mowbray Ridge exposing an old debris flow of mud and rock.

Figure 78. (Right) Small remnants of what used to be a large white dune cordon (see Fig. 59), seen looking west across Hout Bay Beach.

up the beaches around Cape Town (Fig. 58). During large storms beach sand can move
offshore into sandbars and during northwest winter storms sand can move south rather
than north; but averaged over the year, the net transport of beach sand is to the north,
with the sand traversing about 100 m each year. Therefore, beaches that appear stable
to us on an afternoon's visit are in fact highly dynamic systems, with beach sand readily
– and sometimes, during a major storm, very rapidly – moved about. Beach erosion can
result in the loss of sand from tourist beaches and in major storms can destroy coastal
structures. For this reason, a good coastal development practice is to allow building only
on the landward side of stable, vegetated dunes, which act as natural storm barriers.

Development in coastal areas has altered the natural flow of sand. For example, the
headland bypass dune that moves sand from Hout Bay Beach to Sandy Bay (Fig. 59) has
been effectively shut off by the planting of dune grass on Hout Bay Beach (Fig. 78). The
sand destined for Sandy Bay is now accumulating as a large dune in Hout Bay. How
significant this amount of sand is to the total sand transported along the coast is
debatable, but it emphasises the point that when we alter a natural system it has many
consequences, some unanticipated.

People have lived in the Cape Town area for at least the last 200 000 years and until recently have had a relatively minor impact on the environment. Rapid population growth and the large demand for natural resources are resulting in an alarming increase in habitat destruction, loss of biodiversity and pollution. Extrapolation of these trends does not bode well for future Cape Town generations. Most of these detrimental consequences were not anticipated and we are only now starting to comprehend just how complex and interrelated the natural world is.

The rapid loss of species diversity through habitat destruction is a worldwide problem and concern, particularly in highly diverse ecosystems such as the Cape fynbos. In the Cape, the loss of biodiversity is further accelerated by the rapid and widespread invasion of alien plants. Alien plants diminish the ecosystem by decreasing biodiversity and by increasing soil erosion and loss of precious water. The invasion of the fynbos ecosystem by alien plants must be urgently contained.

If the detrimental impacts of our activities go unchecked, then we may well be responsible for a mass extinction event on a par with the asteroid impacts and enormous volcanic outpourings of the past. But, as in the past, Earth and its biosphere

Figure 79. The Cape of Good Hope and Cape Point at the southern end of the Cape Peninsula, looking north. Devil's Peak can be seen on the distant horizon to the right.

will carry on with the large vacancies in ecosystems refilled by the evolution of new species. Viewed on the long geological timescale of millions of years, our impacts will fade away. However reassuring it might be that we are unlikely to destroy Earth's biosphere completely, it would be a sad way to go, particularly for the final generations living in a degraded world.

There are many ways in which we can slow down and perhaps eventually reverse the deterioration of environments in Cape Town: by weeding out alien plants through efforts such as the Working for Water Programme; by cleaning up factory and motor vehicle emissions before they enter rivers or the atmosphere; by using alternative energy sources to fossil fuels; and by practising water conservation. If the view of some economists is correct that human behaviour is largely governed by greed and fear, then the true total cost of resources – namely, production costs as well as ecological costs – must be charged to consumers. Higher costs will reduce consumption (especially excessive consumption) and provide funding for restoration. The city of Cape Town is moving in this direction by instituting a tiered scale for water usage, by spending money on educating people in water conservation and by helping to rid the area of alien vegetation. Intensification of these efforts would go a long way to ensure the preservation of the unique beauty and splendour of Cape Town.

ACKNOWLEDGEMENTS

Most of my understanding of the local geology was gained through interaction with colleagues and students at the University of Cape Town. In addition to the students with all of their insightful questions, I am indebted to the staff of the Geological Sciences, in particular John Rogers and Dave Reid for their excellent field trips and field guides. For broadening my horizon beyond the rocks, I thank Mike Meadows, Judy Sealy, Julia Lee-Thorp, Peter Holmes and other co-instructors of the first-year course I convened: An Introduction to the Earth and Environmental Sciences. I am also grateful for the financial support provided by the University of Cape Town and the National Research Foundation, which funded postgraduate students and numerous research projects on the geology of the West Coast. Mike Meadows, John Rogers and Maarten de Wit provided valuable feedback. I am grateful to Fiona Hinds of Cape Mountain Meanders, and Justin Hyland and George de Greef of ComputaMaps, for generously allowing me to make use of their images. And special thanks to Jenny Sandler for her skilful work on the illustrations and design.

ILLUSTRATION CREDITS

Figure 1. © 2004 F.J. Hinds; Cape Mountain Meanders cc (www.cmm.co.za)

Figure 2. © Mark Skinner; Bateleur Publishing cc

Figure 4. Courtesy of ComputaMaps (www.computamaps.com)

Figure 7. Courtesy NASA/GSFC (credit: J Descloitres) www.visibleearth.nasa.gov

Figure 8(a). Courtesy of ComputaMaps (www.computamaps.com)

Figure 8(b). Adapted from Figure 1.1 of A.P.G. Söhnge, The Cape Fold Belt: Perspective. In: A.P.G. Söhnge and I.W. Hälbich (eds.), Geodynamics of the Cape Fold Belt, Special Publication No. 12, The Geological Society of South Africa, Johannesburg (1983); and J.N. Theron and J.C. Loock, Devonian Deltas of the Cape Supergroup, South Africa. In: M.J. McMillan, A.F. Embry and D.J. Glass (eds.), Devonian of the World I, Memoir 14, Canadian Society of Petroleum Geology, Calgary, Canada (1988)

Figure 9. Courtesy of NASA/JPL-Caltech/NIMA

Figure 11. Adapted from L.H. Kellogg, B.H. Hager and R. D. van der Hilst, Compositional stratification in the deep mantle, Science 283, 1881-1884, Copyright (1999) with permission from AAAS

Figure 12. From S.P. Grand, R.D. van der Hilst and S. Widiyantoro, Global Seismic Tomography: A Snapshot of Convection in the Earth. GSA Today, Vol. 7, Copyright (1997) Geological Society of America

Figure 13. © 2004 F.J. Hinds; Cape Mountain Meanders cc (www.cmm.co.za) based on data from the National Geophysical Data Center (www.ngdc.noaa.gov)

Figure 14. © Mark Skinner; Bateleur Publishing cc

Figure 28. © 2004 F.J. Hinds; Cape Mountain Meanders cc (www.cmm.co.za)

Figure 39(b). Courtesy of Dr John Rogers

Additional Readings

The following books are recommended for those readers interested in learning more.

Yeld, J. and Barker, M. Mountains in the Sea. Table Mountain to Cape Point: An Interpretive Guide to the Table Mountain National Park. SA National Parks, 2004 (An information-packed guide to all of the sites of the park.)

Lundy, M. Best Walks in the Cape Peninsula. Struik, 1999

Cowling, R. and Richardson, D. Fynbos: South Africa's Unique Floral Kingdom. Fernwood Press, Vlaeberg, 1995

Pauw, A. and Johnson, S. Table Mountain: A Natural History. Fernwood Press, Vlaeberg, 1999

(Two large picture books with text describing the fynbos ecosystem)

Smith, A., Malherbe, C., Guenther, M. and Berens, P. The Bushmen of Southern Africa: A Foraging Society in Transition. David Philip Publishers, Cape Town, 2000 (A history of the original inhabitants of the Western Cape and their relation to later arrivals)

Leakey, R. and Lewin, R. The Sixth Extinction. Doubleday, New York, 1995 (A well-written discussion of the present and past mass extinctions of life on Earth)

General books on the geology of southern Africa:

McCarthy, T. and Rubidge, B. The Story of Earth & Life: A southern African perspective on a 4.6-billion-year journey. Struik Publishers, Cape Town, 2005

MacRae, C. Life Etched in Stone: Fossils of South Africa. The Geological Society of South Africa. Johannesburg, 1999 (A beautifully illustrated story of South African rocks and their fossils)

MacPhee, D. and de Wit, M. How the Cape Got its Shape. MapStudio, Cape Town, 2003 (A colourful fold-out poster on the geology of the Cape Peninsula)

Cole, D.I. The Building Stones of Cape Town: A Geological Walking Tour. Council for Geoscience, Popular Geoscience Series 3, 2002

Viljoen, M.J. and Reimold, W.U. An Introduction to South Africa's Geological and Mining Heritage. The Geological Society of South Africa and Mintek, Randburg, 1999 (A well-illustrated guide to South African geology)

Hendey, Q.B. Langebaanweg: A Record of Past Life. South African Museum, Cape Town, 1982 (A general summary of the fossils from the Langebaanweg phosphate quarry and the story they tell of past life in the area)

Norman, N. and Whitfield, G. Geological Journeys: A traveller's guide to South
    Africa's rocks and landforms. Struik Publishers, Cape Town, 2006

Two geology guidebooks are available from the Department of Geological
Sciences, University of Cape Town (www.uct.ac.za/depts/geolsci):
Rogers, J. and Hartnady, C.J.H. Cape Peninsula Geological Excursion Guide.
    Department of Geological Sciences, University of Cape Town, 1996
Rogers, J., Minter, W.E.L. and Reid, D.L. The Geology of the Western Cape.
    Department of Geological Sciences, University of Cape Town, 1996

Two guidebooks are also available on Namibia's geology:
Grünert, N. Namibia. Fascination of Geology: A Travel Handbook. Klaus Hess
    Publishers, 2000
Schneider, G. The Roadside Geology of Namibia. Gebrüder Borntraeger,
    Berlin, 2004

Detailed and technical publications on the geology of southern Africa:
Armstrong, R., de Wit, M.J., Reid, D., York D. and Zartman, R. Cape Town's
    Table Mountain reveals rapid Pan-African uplift of its basement rocks.
    Journal of African Earth Sciences, Volume 27 (pages 10–11), 1998 (Source
    of zircon radiometric ages)
De Wit, M.J. and Ransome, I.G.D. (eds.). Inversion Tectonics of the Cape Fold
    Belt, Karoo and Cretaceous Basins of Southern Africa. A.A. Balkema,
    Rotterdam, Netherlands, 1992 (A collection of detailed geology papers)
Tankard, A.J., Jackson, M.P.A., Eriksson, K.A., Hobday, D.K., Hunter, D.R. and
    Minter, W.E.L. Crustal Evolution of Southern Africa: 3.8 Billion Years of
    Earth History. Springer-Verlag, New York, 1982 (An overview of southern
    Africa geology)
Theron, J.N., Gresse, P.G., Siegfried, H.P. and Rogers, J. The Geology of the
    Cape Town Area (Explanation: Sheet 3318, 1:250 000). Geological Survey.
    Department of Mineral and Energy Affairs, 1992 (A detailed summary of
    the geology of the Cape Town area available (along with map) from the
    Council for Geoscience, Bellville)
Partridge, T.C. and Maud, R.R. The Cenozoic of Southern Africa. Oxford
    Monographs on Geology and Geophysics No. 40, Oxford University Press,
    New York, 2000 (A collection of papers on the rock record of the last
    65 million years)

Figure 80. Geological map of Cape Town and environs.

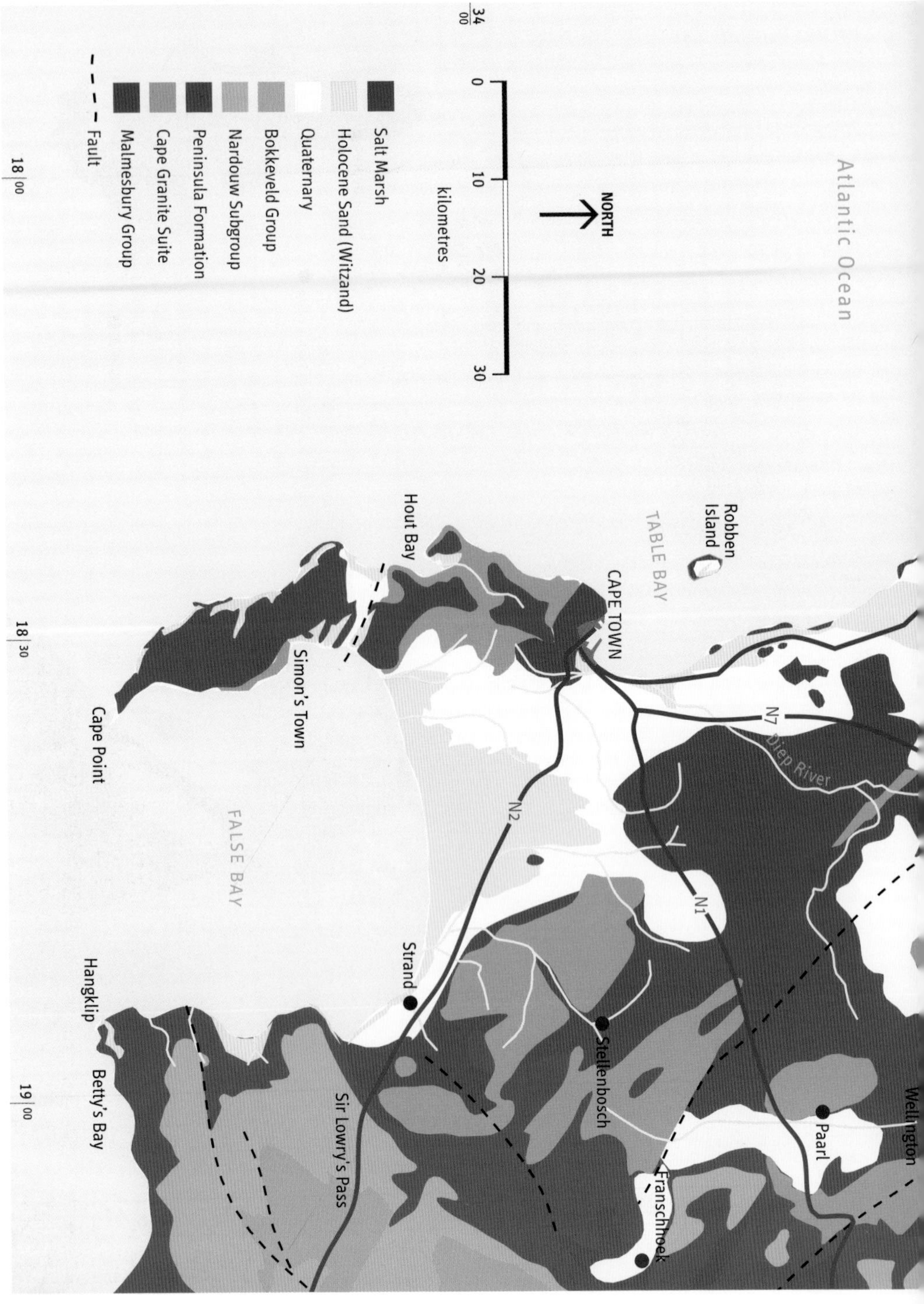

Salt Marsh
Holocene Sand (Witzand)
Quaternary
Bokkeveld Group
Nardouw Subgroup
Peninsula Formation
Cape Granite Suite
Malmesbury Group

Fault

NORTH

kilometres

0   10   20   30

34
00

18
00

18
30

19
00

Atlantic Ocean

Robben Island

TABLE BAY

CAPE TOWN

Diep River

N7

N1

N2

Hout Bay

Simon's Town

Cape Point

FALSE BAY

Strand

Stellenbosch

Franschhoek

Paarl

Wellington

Hangklip

Betty's Bay

Sir Lowry's Pass

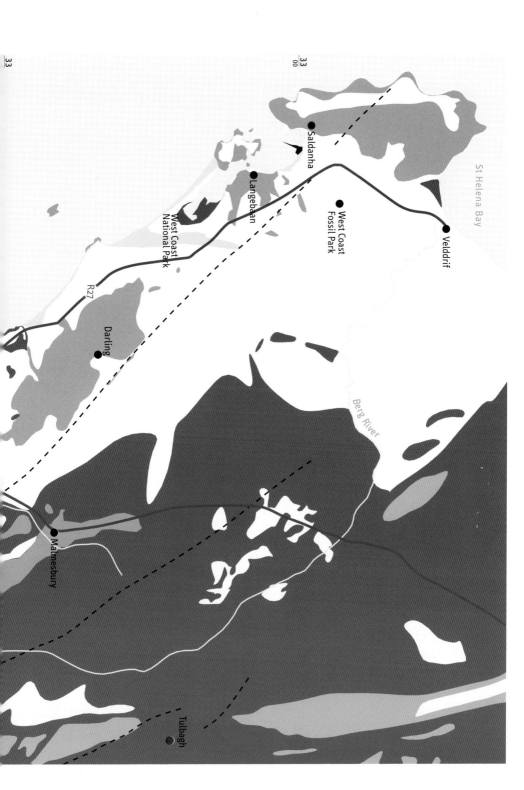

St Helena Bay

Saldanha

Langebaan

West Coast
National Park

West Coast
Fossil Park

Velddrif

R27

Darling

Berg River

Malmesbury

Tulbagh